**HANS KRONB**

# On the Track of Water's Secret

**FROM VIKTOR SCHAUBERGER TO JOHANN GRANDER**

HANS KRONBERGER & SIEGBERT LATTACHER

# On the Track of Water's Secret

FROM VIKTOR SCHAUBERGER TO JOHANN GRANDER

URANUS

© **Copyright** by Uranus Verlagsgesellschaft m. b. H., Vienna, 1995

**Layout & DTP:** Julia Posch & Mag. Karl Hintermeier
Umwelt Media Consult, Christian Müller.
**English translation:** Ann Dubsky
**Reader:** Murray Hall
**Print:** Wiener Verlag, Himberg
**Distribution for Austria:** Mohr Morawa, Vienna
**Distribution for Germany and Switzerland:** Michaels Vertrieb, D-86971, Peiting
All rights reserved. This book, or parts thereof, may not be reproduced in any form without the permission of the publisher.
**ISBN** 3-901626-03-4

# Table of Contents

# Foreword

T his book is definitely not the final word in the search for the answer to the secrets hidden in water. It is far more a detailed beginning. The water puzzle is actually a human puzzle. This became clear soon after research began, since it is inseparably bound to the question whether there are human beings who possess knowledge that it is impossible to acquire based on the current state of science?

The answer to this is: in the first place, findings on previously unknown characteristics and effects of water are not to be found in text books and secondly, the water observers and researchers concerned with here are people who have no university level education whatsoever.

The main question is therefore: is there any such thing as human beings who can see into a different time or into a different configuration of space? And simply by observation, intuition and interpretation of natural phenomena and natural relationships recognize more than the entire scientific apparatus with its megaprocessors and its research budgets amounting to billions?

A few years ago my answer would have been a clear-cut, "Absolutely not. All nonsense." In the meantime, the evidence has piled up. Water will be the elixir of the third millennium. If for no other reason, it deserves special attention. Should the theories in this book be disproved, then this publication will turn out to be just one more book among many. Aside from a few hundred kilograms of paper, nothing will have been lost. But if there should be something to it then the discussion this book will provoke about previously unknown characteristics and powers in water will not come to a halt.

There have always been people who knew things they could not have learned by methods known to us. Paracelsus was one of them. An extremely successful doctor and an outcast in the scientific world, he wrote treatises five hundred years ago that only much later were recognized as being valid and which are gaining enormously in importance again today. Up until only recently, homeopathic and conventional medicine excluded one another; today they complement each other. Perhaps we are standing at the threshold of entirely new knowledge that in turn may be mostly old knowledge that has lain buried.

Despite all the personal reserve that is the most important prerequisite for journalistic professionalism, I was not able to resist the questions and the findings of the two naturalists, Viktor Schauberger and Johann Grander, for long. Viktor Schauberger has observed water and seen and recorded more than all the scientific instruments put together so far. Johann Grander revitalizes or energizes water by transforming it with high frequency oscillations created by a special magnetic motor he developed himself, and there are innumerable user testimonies that report unbelievable results. The two naturalists are completely different from each other and yet, not really.

I have been collecting reports for more than three years, have been present at experiments and have talked to both ordinary people and scientists about water.

My original approach to the subject was an amused astonishment that sometimes independently broke into respectful shivers. It is not my task to pass judgment, but instead to make the collected knowledge accessible to other people. Seen this way, mine is the most wonderful profession in the world.

Siegbert Lattacher addressed the water secret by way of literature; that is a much more intellectual approach than mine. We have put the collected material together harmoniously and thus intensified it. The officially authorized expert for technical chemistry, Horst Felsch, approaches the secret of water from the point of view of science. He has read the work critically, demanded strict distance to sheer assumptions and all too euphoric statements. We have devoted a chapter to the equally astonishing and fascinating results of his research.

*Hans Kronberger*
*November 15, 1995*

# CHAPTER 1

# Secrets within Secrets

D oes water have mysterious powers we have not recognized so far? And if so, how do they manifest themselves? How do they work, how can we put them to use? Most scientists and water experts deny that water has these powers. In their opinion water is simply water. It has the chemical formula $H_2O$ and has been researched in every way known to science. On the other hand, there are the so-called naturalists with no higher scientific education, who maintain that water is anything but merely water, quite the contrary. It has powers we know only very little about, it harbors secrets that are greater than all of our present wisdom put together.

Water, according to these naturalists, is much more than the chemical formula $H_2O$. It is the foundation of all life on earth and it resonates in constant harmony with the universe. Yes, it vibrates internally and it transports energy and information of colossal proportions. Reducing water to a simple chemical formula is, for these naturalists, a blind approach to a complicated form of matter. Water changes its properties constantly, can both benefit and harm people, can make them well and sick, can absorb and give off energy. It is the most fascinating element and at the same time, the one on which the least research has been done, the least is known. Naturalists and traditional scientists agree only that water is essential to life, but while the former dwell on the aspect of quality, most scientists are satisfied with merely stating that the presence of water is enough to ensure life processes on earth.

Naturalists are urged on by reports of the experiences gathered by users of specially treated water which has produced effects the present state of science cannot begin to explain. This covers a wide range of areas, including health matters, vegetation and high technology. There are even reports on large-scale tests in China that tell of saving energy and achieving better emission levels for diesel locomotives by using technologies involving "revitalized" water. Here again, present-day science is unable to supply a suitable explanation. But the results can be measured.

The data are so dense and wide-reaching that before long there will be no getting around a treatment (including a scientific one) of this subject, even if only to bring the discussion to an end. The intention of this book is to make the available material accessible and to offer it for discussion. Enthusiastic proponents of "Wasserbelebung" or revitalizing water may be somewhat taken aback by the authors' reserve, but it is indispensable if a clear and fair picture of the current state of the dispute over the effects of water is to be presented. Much of the contents speaks for itself. Of course everyone is free to view the observations on the effects of water presented here very critically. Any effort to disprove the theories involved is welcome. New knowledge grows from contradiction.

The first three reports on the effects of revitalized water sounded highly improbable but not completely absurd. They aroused the author's curiosity about the subject of water. One thing is certain: if they had been the only reports, there would never have been a book about them. Many other reports have since followed them.

Therefore these three accounts of personal experiences are placed at the beginning, independently of the system this book employs. This allows the reader to consider whether knowing about these reports would also have caused him or her to take up the search to discover water's mysteries.

As a matter of principle, only reports made by people who stand behind their experiences with their full names and full identities were accepted. This makes it possible to reconstruct and question these experiences.

Marianne Lackner is a young farm woman from the Palten Valley in Styria. The handwritten report of her experiences with "revitalized water" (for a definition of this term, see Chapter 4) using the methods devised by the Tyrolean naturalist, Johann Grander, sounds so improbable that it would normally have landed in the editorial room waste basket. The time is not ripe for such far-reaching experiences as those of Marianne Lackner. Placed in the fabric of similar types of reports, however, one cannot avoid having to take a serious look at these phenomena.

The notes jotted down like entries in a diary by the young woman from Trieben in Styria could easily have been passed off as products of a vivid imagination or at best explained away in medical terms as a placebo effect, in a realm where expectation actually results in healing (in the Bible this process is explained with "faith can move mountains"), if other people had not had similar experiences that occurred later under similar circumstances.

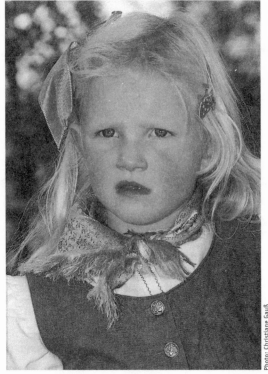

Melanie
Lackner

Photo: Christiane Gauß

13

Marianne Lackner had a water revitalizing device made by Johann Grander built into her water supply system. Parallel to this, she consumed a Grander water concentrate, so-called Grander water in the blue bottle. She kept a kind of diary of her experiences. This was, incidentally, long before she could have dreamed that they might possibly be of journalistic interest. Her writing is correspondingly unaffected. "One day a nice man we didn't know at all, stood at the kitchen door. It was late afternoon on a Thursday. I, Marianne, and my mother were getting ready to go to the farmers' market in Trieben. I was almost not able to go, since I had a terrible crick in the neck. Couldn't turn my head at all. Then the good man asked, can I try something? He hung his water necklace around me, also brought out a webbed band [ed: filled with Grander concentrate] and wrapped it around my neck. When he hung the water pendant on me I got very nervous for just an instant. But I was very calm again right away. We dropped what we were doing and devoted all our attention to this Herr Rauscher. To our surprise, this man was never forward - genuinely pleasant.

"After about 10 minutes I could already turn my head a little to the right and by the time Herr Rauscher left, it seemed almost as though it had all blown away. He left me the band for the night. I lay on it that evening when I went to sleep and the next day I felt as though nothing had ever been wrong with me. Simply super!"

Following this "success," the Lackner family had the water revitalizing apparatus built into their water supply system and started experimenting with energized water. Their first test object was their daughter, Melanie. Marianne Lackner wrote, "My daughter Melanie had suffered from neurodermatitis since she was 5 months old. No doctor could help her. I wouldn't even begin to let them prescribe cortisone salves. It would get better and then worse, and that went on until she drank a few sips of water [Grander water] with me on this particular Thursday.

"She also had another illness. Ever since Easter Sunday, she had suffered from anemia caused by fever suppositories (2 of them) that were prescribed for high fever. She was in bed for two days with almost 42 degrees [Celsius] fever. After the suppositories, she started to have hallucinations for 2-3 hours, so I didn't give her any more. From that point on, the child hardly ate or drank anything. When she tried to eat, since she was hungry after all, she'd swallow a bite and then scream she had a stomach ache and lie down again. That went on for 2 weeks until I was really frightened. I thought the child ought to go to the hospital, but I was even more afraid of that.

"So, she drank a sip of water with me and suddenly she took her blanket and went to bed. Pretty soon, she came back again and drank a few times more. Suddenly the spots on her face from neuro-dermatitis got very red, everywhere where she had the spots, but only briefly, then they got white and could hardly be seen anymore. Next day they were all gone and since then she has not had any at all."

During the following weeks, the serious skin ailment disappeared completely and the fever dropped quickly: "You could watch it happening. The next moment she got pink cheeks and a pink chin and by around 9 that evening she was as lively as could be, started to sing, something she hadn't done at all for several weeks. It was like a miracle. We couldn't believe it, but that's exactly the way it was. Just wonderful. The next day she started to eat again and she gained a few kilograms."

Marianne Lackner also sees success in her own therapy: "And things were happening to me during the same period, too. I had suffered from a bad left ovary for several years (strong pains when my feet got cold). Suddenly, after I drank the water, I got such a sharp pain in the left ovary, it took my breath away. But this pain did not last long; I drank a sip of water again, put my hand on the same place but I could not feel any more pain. They had just blown away, as though they had never even existed!"

Frau Lackner made her next observation in the barn. "We had to sell a female calf about 2 years old, because she never came in heat. In the stall next to her was the friend she grew up with, also female. They went up to the mountain pasture together and always stood next to each other. The black spotted one was already carrying though, and had dropped her first calf on January 23. In March, the brown cow was sold. From this day on, her friend - the black spotted cow Stella - stopped eating and drinking. That went on for 4-5 days. Whenever it was feeding time, the animal would lie down. She got so weak she could hardly stay on her feet. All at once her milk was gone. We didn't know what to do. This cow was emotionally sick. Then we got the idea of putting Grander water in the drinking trough. It took a lot of effort before the animal drank it. But then she starting lapping at it. The next day Mother put the water in a large bowl and Stella drank it all. The day after that she drank 2 bowlfuls. Then she also started eating again. The milk came back, too. The water must have helped her get over her emotional pain."

Successful experiments were not limited to the immediate environment. A visitor was also treated. "One day we had visitors from Leoben. One of them was an elderly woman, 68 years old and totally emaciated. Mother offered them bread spread with fresh crackling-lard and some Grander water. Our acquaintance just happened to mention that this woman had already been operated on her gall bladder 5 times and once on her stomach. Since then she throws up every bit of food she eats. Oh, dear, we thought, since we didn't know about that beforehand. But she ate the bread and drank 2 glasses of the water. But we were wrong about what we thought. She did not go to the toilet to vomit, not even at home. From that day on, she hasn't vomited again. She did have to go to the toilet several times that same evening though, since she had diarrhea; that was the reaction to the water, the cleansing of so many medicines. On June 5 our acquaintance called again to ask if she could have some more water. Her aunt was completely happy, hadn't vomited at all for 5 weeks, had already gained weight besides, and felt absolutely fine. Doesn't take medicines any more, either. No doctor could help her, and the water helped over night."

Marianne Lackner and her whole family with her, with mother Gertrude Lackner at the head, began observing their entire surroundings and were able to see changes in both animals and plants. In passing, she describes the successful treatment of a neighbor's child:

"Meanwhile a young friend of a neighbor in the village came and got some of our Grander water. She had two daughters, 6 1/2 and 2

1/2 years old. One of them was in the first grade of primary school. All of a sudden, Astrid started drinking more water. After a short time, her mother noticed that Astrid's worms began to leave her body. And not just a few, some 40 of them."

In another place in her report, she describes the effect on chickens: "After we connected the water revitalization apparatus on April 29, 1994, the chickens got some of the energized water, too. All of a sudden there were 3 – 4 eggs more in the nests, and the old hens began to lay again. And the roosters started acting crazy besides, but not to our disadvantage. Otherwise they would have landed in the soup pot."

In addition the Lackner family noticed that the flowers watered with revitalized water no longer needed any fertilizer: "...even the flowers that should have landed in the compost by then began to sprout again, have meanwhile put on growth, and some of them have started blooming again."

Marianne Lackner's accounts sound extremely imaginative, if not downright fantastic. As stated earlier, seen as a single observation

The Lackner family from Trieben in Styria with UVO advisor, Fritz Rauscher

Photo: Christiane Gauß

they would hardly be important. But meanwhile, there are many, many letters of this kind (also see Chapter 5: Revitalized Water and Health).

The first question, and one that is decisive in many respects, is: can the Lackner family draw personal advantages from their claims about the effects of revitalized water, in short, do they also deal in revitalized water or Grander products? The result of investigations was a clear no. The sales company UVO (Umweltvertriebsorganisation: tr. Environmental Marketing Organization) which deals exclusively in Grander products, can prove without doubt that the Lackner family has no commercial interest in spreading positive information about revitalizing water.

The next question concerns the unassuming gentleman who brought revitalized water into the house. He was the 46 year-old UVO associate, Fritz Rauscher, who made the first contact through one of the family's neighbors he knew. It was also he who saw to it that Marianne Lackner's notes, which were originally not intended for publication, got to us.

Of course, the accounts require examination. A visit to the Lackner family should clarify the matter. It takes place on Saturday, September 9, 1995, at 11 o'clock in the morning.

The Lackner farm turns out to be a model of the idyllic homestead, beautifully situated on a south slope, the color of magnificent flowers everywhere, a fountain flowing in front of the well cared for, old farmhouse. A big, happy family, headed by the grandmother, Gertrude Lackner. Marianne Lackner cooks while her two little daughters, the four year-old Melanie and her 6 year-old sister sweep through the room, their straw-colored blond braids waving in the air.

To the question of how Marianne Lackner's mother-in-law saw little Melanie's story, she gives an answer that is both detailed and precise. She describes the child's behavior exactly. The doctors couldn't think of anything to do except prescribe fever suppositories and the child's eyes had already begun to look dull. Admitting Melanie to hospital, a decision they all feared, seemed unavoidable. Her account duplicates that of her daughter-in-law to a rare degree of exactness. Gertrude Lackner makes a very reliable impression. When asked if there was a doctor who could confirm the presence of neurodermatitis, she replied that there were photographs of the child showing the skin disease and that anyone could see how Melanie looks today. She had gone from doctor to doctor, had tried everything, taken all the medicines except for the cortisone salve which they were afraid of. Melanie had hideous pustules on her face and was completely disfigured. The photographs are brought for evidence. Unfortunately, these turn out to be two rather bad pictures (apparently made with old film), but the severity of the skin disease is clearly discernible (see p. 67).

We talk about a half a dozen similar cases which have come up in the meanwhile, such as a young girl's severe case of acne. She wore men's shirts with sleeves that were too long so she could hide her hands, and she covered her face with her long hair. After a "water treatment" the acne disappeared, says Gertrude Lackner. And another case: a kidney patient who requires dialysis and has been waiting for a donor kidney for three years. She drinks the water in secret since she does not dare admit this unscientific "infidelity" to her doctor. A short while ago, she produced urine again for the first time, a development naturally attributed to the effects of medication. But the important thing is not the cause, it is the success.

In Gertrude Lackner's opinion, the effect of revitalizing fresh well water is optimal. She had the water that comes from her two wells behind the house tested in Graz. There it was said that the water was of such an extremely high quality that it could be given to babies without hesitation.

And then there was also the 68 year-old woman from Leoben who had suffered from nausea since she was 18. Could she be reached? She was a friend of a family from Leoben who only came to Trieben on weekends, but Gertrude Lackner would be glad to make the contact. The woman from Leoben was Charlotte Schimek. She was following a strict diet after her stomach and gall bladder operations. She reported that she had eaten the bread with lard at the Lackner's intentionally, thinking she would have to throw it up anyway. Instead, she felt the soothing effects of the water at once. She repeats Marianne Lackner's accounts to the letter. For the last six months she had barely vomited and had even gained weight. Friends of hers had brought her water regularly from the Lackner farm some 50 kilometers away. However, after six months the effects wore off, and vomiting started again. The doctors told her she would have to live with this ailment since bile was flowing into her stomach. Then she stopped drinking the water, since getting it was too troublesome.

And the neighbor with the child with worms? "That's the easiest thing in the world," said Frau Lackner. "We only need to call her up, she wouldn't have any objections to telling her story."

And that's also the way it turned out.

No one in the family regards these phenomena as a "miracle," but "only" as a "natural" effect of the water they are happy about.

A few simple ideas arise in connection with these experiences. Shouldn't we try to find our way back to having faith in the possibility of mobilizing the body's own powers of healing rather than delegating health problems to third persons exclusively? Perhaps there ought to be a branch of medicine that could be called placebo healing. Why not, actually? There are forms of mental treatment that have long been recognized by conventional medicine, in which nothing material is involved, "only" consolation, encouragement, or in the case of children the loving presence of relatives in a hospital. These methods of healing or support for the healing process may be bad for the pharmaceutical industry, but are so widely accepted today that they are no longer a subject for discussion. But isn't it also a situation where something flows from one human being to another, or from a person's spirit to his own matter when he gives himself a "good talking to," assures himself that he will make it. The recognition of a flow of thought that can change a person's frame of mind, either for good or for bad, should at least open up theoretical prospects for a so-called transfer of information about matter. But this is just a side thought.

If this book results in more bright minds and great intellects concerning themselves with water again, its objective will have been fulfilled. The main thing is that experiences and testimonies about water are made available to a wide audience and to research. The paramount goal is: a prudent handling of water should be activated for the good of mankind. This publication should also encourage users who have kept silent for fear of being thought insane to reveal their experiences. (We ran into this phenomenon of keeping silent again and again during our research.)

Above all, science is challenged to investigate these occurrences. Not so much because man ought to examine absolutely everything - in many cases it would be enough for science to be satisfied with knowing about the effects without being primarily interested in looking for the exact formula behind them - but because the scientific thirst for knowledge is basically positive as long as the findings that result from it are used to the benefit of mankind.

Today the conservative wing of natural scientists takes the stand that the only thing that is valid is that which stands up to empirical examination and that can be repeated and re-created at will. This will not be possible with revitalized water for a long time to come since it always reacts "differently." As it is, modern research from Albert Einstein to the chaos theory already starts with the premise that a causality (an immediately reconstructable connection) only functions in the macrocosms, but not in the microcosms. In short, there is no "final" and "irrefutable" claim to knowledge. That would mean that man had reached the end, that there is no new basic knowledge, that research can no longer lead to a correction of existing knowledge, but at best to a refinement of the mechanisms already known. This standpoint would also mean the end of scientific curiosity and this, in turn, the end of human development. Albert Einstein even went so far as to say that when the last formula is discovered, it will be the end of the world.

But the beginnings of a process of re-thinking are in evidence. In medicine (where the view of the body as a whole organism is coming into the foreground again, in place of repairs to single parts, and treating with homeopathic dosages instead of chemical bludgeons), in agriculture (organic production taking the phases of the moon and ancient knowledge about chemical-free pest control into account) and even in physics where the realization that the whole is more than the sum of its parts has become established.

Labeling phenomena as fundamentally impossible only because they cannot be proven today, at least with today's methods, is, to put it mildly, short-sighted. For instance, who would have thought it possible a hundred years ago for an apparatus only slightly larger than the fist, called a cellular phone, would make it possible to speak with America, that is transport words through space with no sign of a cable, even send pictures along with them? Anyone who had proposed this more than 60 years ago would have been declared insane. Why should anyone, therefore, regard the claims of naturalists that water can also receive, store and transport information impossible at the outset, or to rule out the possibility altogether?

The second example comes from industry. The effects are observed in the realm of technology and are measured by engineers. The causes of these effects cannot be explained by modern-day science yet, either. In the Vienna headquarters of the confectionery producers, Casali-Napoli (Manner) water revitalization has been used in the refrigeration system since 1992. Industry is concerned with facts and figures alone, and the food industry has to cope with the added element of strict hygiene regulations. For that reason, the closed circuit cooling systems are worth special attention. The head of technical matters, Helmut Ondricek, describes the results as follows: "On July 21, 1992, we installed a water revitalization device into the cooling water circuit. After about four days we were able to stop adding chemicals completely. Up to that time we had to use three different kinds of chemical additives. The biggest problem up to this point was the slime bacteria that settled in the refrigerator's soil trap. About 10 to 15 work-hours were needed for cleaning every week. After activating the water energizer for about two weeks, the amount of slime bacteria regressed. At the same time we noticed an increase in calcareous substances and rust in the water. After about five to six weeks there was no slime bacteria detectable and there were also no more hardened residues. In September of 1992, we were able to stop cleaning the soil traps and filters entirely. Then we opened a condenser of one refrigerator and were unable to find any more deposits (sludge, incrustations) in the pipes. The lid of the condenser had a number of shiny metallic places. Previously we had to empty the cooling water containers twice a year and clean them, but now all the deposits, except for the primer, had disappeared in all the places that come in contact with revitalized water. Slime bacteria disperse by themselves. The water is soft, it does not smell bad any more, it is invigorating, refreshing on the skin although it is water that circulates in a closed system.

"We made additional tests with a machine that washes molds. The plastic molds were being attacked by high additions of detergents and gloss dryers and the high temperatures (90 degrees Celsius). After installing water revitalization, we were able to reduce the temperature to 60 degrees and after 14 days omit the gloss dryer. In figures, this amounts to a saving of about 400,000 Austrian Schillings (roughly 40,000 dollars) a year on chemicals no longer used. The water revitalization devices paid for themselves within a short time." This statement was made in 1993. In the meanwhile, other industrial plants have also installed water revitalization systems (see chapter 6, Effects in Technical Areas).

Despite the fact that it must be assumed that the manager of the company would long before have deterred the enthusiastic foreman from continuing his "games" if they hadn't paid off, the results and Ondricek's experiences must be looked at critically.

First of all it would be interesting to know where Ondricek got his first experience with "water revitalization?" His answer: "From an acquaintance who used it for the first time in a bakery in St. Pölten for an oven used for steaming bread rolls. They had an enormous problem with the steam leaving calcified deposits. The plumber had to clean this oven almost every week. My friend wanted to install a traditional decalcification system, but he was urged to use the Grander water revitalization system. And it worked. At the beginning only a little, but then a point was reached where there were no more calcified deposits. This man approached me, since he knew about the situation in our plant. I was extremely doubtful in the beginning."

After the motto, "if you do it, do it right," he tested the water on his wife, too: "The first positive experience I had with revitalized water was connected with health. My wife had problems with her digestion and her circulation. She drank the Grander water and it alleviated her symptoms. I was aware that I would be taking a big risk at the plant, and that there would be the danger of a possible break-down. But the success was compelling and I began to take a serious interest in water revitalization by suggesting to Hans Grander that he develop a water revitalization system for industrial use." The previous systems were made for use in households; a special, larger system was constructed. "In the plant I had my first experience with water revitalization in the cooling water circuit and then we started using it in other areas, too. For the mold washer, in the boiler house where it also brought good improvement, saving on material and time. We made a surprising observation: the heat conductivity of the water changed and I was able to show an energy saving of 5-7% in the refrigerating system."

The engineer Ondricek had only one explanation for the effect: "For me, this is homeopathy in the broadest sense, a transfer of information on a molecular level, which according to Hans Grander can only function in living things, but not in dead matter (i.e., heavy metals such as zinc, cadmium or lead). Besides savings of about 400,000 Schillings on chemicals no longer needed, we also notice savings in maintenance work (now only 10 - 15 hours a half year compared with that much in a week previously). We had a machine that for no discernible reason would break down after 8 - 10 hours of use. The service people couldn't say why, either. But since the installation of water revitalization this problem has vanished.

Personal experience is also important for Helmut Ondricek. "My wife and I have been drinking Grander water every day for about four years. I notice a positive change in myself. Before, I was very restless and irritable, now I can cope much better at the plant, and my co-workers wonder about the changes in me."

The circumstantial evidence on the effects of revitalized water is massive, there is no doubt whatsoever about that. It does not come from "crackpots". Though some of these did show up, too, they were quickly sorted out. Most of those who reported on the effects tended to be reserved, serious people.

The health aspect is certainly the most problematic in the use of

Helmut Ondricek,
the Napoli-Casali company

Photo: Bernhard Wartinger

revitalized water. It cannot be standardized, there are no norms for results, and naturally no exact scientific explanation that allows for duplicating an effect. The reference to a similarity with homeopathy can be seen as an explanatory bridge, but it is not completely satisfactory. Most important, it raises the question of whether homeopathy also works on plants. In horticulture and agriculture, especially in organic farming, water is not simply water.

One of the first to look into the relationship between growth, plant quality and revitalized water is the Salzburg organic farmer, Johann Feldinger. Practicing pure organic farming methods, that is, using no artificial fertilizers, no chemical pesticides or chemical insecticides, he cultivates salad cress in the only farm of its kind in Austria. His faith in these powers is unshakable. He reports on his experiences with enlivened water: "I turned to revitalized water because someone told me about a machine that stimulates the soil, water and plants. I got one of these systems right away for my business - we grow organically - and that makes it necessary to give life to the plants, for example through revitalized water, and this brought us a step forward, that's important for the life of the soil. The soil is harmonious, we do not use artificial fertilizer any more at all, only compost and energized water. With the water revitalization apparatus the cress sprouts much quicker than with normal water. I think that is due to the information that is supplied by the revitalized water. In winter the cress is mature in six to seven days, when it used to take 10 days. The cress is much stronger and darker, has more flavor and therefore sells better. I had the cress examined for vital qualities and there is an enormous difference to what is normally seen. The people at the laboratory couldn't say why the cress was so big and I told them I use revitalized water. They said it must come from that, they couldn't imagine any other reason.

"The fact that the water has a different quality is seen on the kohlrabi leaves for example. The water sticks to them longer. Before, with water that wasn't revitalized, it all ran off. You can also see how dark and beautiful the kohlrabi is. We used to have problems with humidity in the glass house. Now the air there is very good, a completely normal climate in which plants and people feel comfortable." An expertise made by a chemist, Dr. Fritz M. Balzer (publicly appointed and sworn expert for the evaluation of substances in the soil for the Hessian State Office for Nutrition, Agriculture and Land Development in Kassel), confirms after thorough laboratory analyses a definite difference between "Feldinger's Hausgartl Kresse" ("Feldinger's Home-grown Cress") and conventional cress. Feldinger attributes these convincing results to the combination of the organic method of cultivation he chose and watering with revitalized water.

Anything that's good for his plants, says Johann Feldinger, must also be good for him and his family and he built a water revitalization system into his home. He says before this, the tapwater from the house system was aggressive. He suffered from an allergy that was apparently directly connected with the bath water, since it disappeared whenever he went to Carinthia on vacation. And it disappeared altogether when he installed water revitalization into his private system. Shortly after installation, red water came out of the tap: rust had loosened itself from the pipes. But the sensation as far as the family was concerned, was contributed by his wife. She claims she has been able to reduce the consumption of laundry detergent by 50% since then.

These three examples were the inducement to start a systematic search for the answers to water's riddles. Three unexplainable testimonies, but from people whose credibility cannot be denied. Actually, three puzzles. The first step was the search for historical models. It is known that Paracelsus and Hildegard von Bingen, like almost all the important healers of the past, pointed to the effects of water. However, we asked ourselves: were and are there also personalities who question the traditional scientific view? We came across the Upper Austrian forester, naturalist and natural philosopher, Viktor Schauberger, who is without doubt one of the most fascinating figures of this century.

Organic plant breeder, Johann Feldinger with wife

Photo: Schauberger family

*Viktor Schauberger - The Father of Water Observation*

# CHAPTER 2

# Viktor Schauberger - The Father of Water Observation

*"Towards the end of this millennium, a liter of water*
*will cost more than a liter of wine."*
*(Viktor Schauberger, 1935).*

A t present there is a single biography of Viktor Schauberger written in German.[1]) Despite its shortcomings, it offers a fascinating insight into this naturalist's turbulent life. Regardless of what one may think of his views, his biography provides exciting reading by itself.

Viktor Schauberger, born in 1885, learned to be a forester. Four generations before him had also taken up this occupation. At his father's wish, Viktor even started a university study of forestry, but he instinctively rejected this kind of education and, in the end, passed the state forestry examinations at a forestry school. After that he continued his studies alone in the forest, devoting special attention to water and the creatures that lived in it. His fundamental realization was that hydrologists "do everything backwards". Since he also voiced his opinion in the open, this "scientifically ignorant" forester was soon confronted with an angry phalanx of hydrologists (with the exception of a small group he was personally able to convince) whose vicious opinions he put into relationship this way: "They think I'm crazy. Maybe they're right. In this case, it doesn't matter whether

---

[1]) Olof Alexandersson, Lebendes Wasser, Ennsthaler Verlag, Steyr 1993

there's one fool more or less in the world. But if it so happens that I am right and science is wrong, then may the Lord have mercy on mankind."

Schauberger observed nature and arrived at the opinion that the "explosion technology", the technology of burning and destroying, is basically wrong and absolutely in contradiction to nature. He opposed the idea of internal combustion engines, the "fire-breathing monsters," with that of the power of "implosion." He said the explosion technology "moved wrong", since the process of internal combustion worked centrifugally, destructively and detrimentally to life, it changed natural products of high quality, such as coal and oil into waste products such as ash, cinders and exhaust emissions, which place an enormous burden on the environment and with prolonged use will eventually lead to its destruction. Besides, coal, oil, natural gas and uranium are important building blocks for the geosphere. Nature itself only uses disintegrating forces to decompose sick, weak or unviable elements, in the form of spoilage and decay. But even these processes are in turn the starting point for the development of new, more valuable life. In burning and combustion, this "sacred principle" is interrupted by force. In contrast to this, implosion is a kind of product refinement in which material of poorer quality is transformed into something of greater worth. That is exactly the opposite of the process mechanistic science has chosen. "Nothing explodes in a plant," said Viktor Schauberger. But what is implosion? Implosion is simply the opposite of explosion. All of our present-day technologies and the supply of energy are based on explosion, on "expansion" by producing warmth through burning raw or refined natural materials. Only a small part of the energy contained in these materials can be utilized in this way. The far larger amount disperses into the atmosphere as heat in the form of gases and steam or is left over as residues or ash in or on the soil. These residues, the used products and the wastes caused by large branches of industry, eat away at the earth's supply of water and oxygen and their almost unmanageable volume is leading to the contamination, pollution and putrefaction of organic life on and in the earth, in the water and in the air.

Contrary to centrifugal explosion, implosion works inwards, towards the center, centripetally. It concentrates its power towards the center where it then becomes the strongest. In nature this system is carried out to perfection. We see these processes in all the motions that take place in unimpeded nature. In the water, the wind, in the sap of the trees and in the blood of living creatures, movement does not take an explosive course towards the outside, but an implosive one, towards the inside, concentrating itself at the center. Bodies of water left to flow naturally turn within themselves, make winding movements that breathe and shelter life. They have the striking ability to regenerate waste water that flows into it to a great degree and to revitalize it. And in the whirlwind, as in the whirlpool, the spiral motion is present with a vacuum and low temperatures in the inmost core. The same system is seen in the farthest corners of the universe as "spiral nebula". [2])

Viktor Schauberger recognized this principle while observing trout in water. He tries to explain the puzzle of how a trout can make a standing jump several meters high against the enormous force of a waterfall. His conclusion: the spiraling free-falling water (implosion) creates a wake at the center that tends to go in the opposite direction. The trout searches out this countercurrent. It usually prepares itself by circling in a hollowed out pool that the waterfall enters with a thunderous roar. It circles in curves that become narrower and narrower around this raging activity towards the center of the countercurrent. As soon as it reaches the narrowest place and the mass of falling water opens up a gap for a fraction of a second, it slips through and, sucked up the center by the countercurrent, quickly rushes up the water fall and is thrown up into the air. At the top it lands in calm headwater and continues its journey to the next waterfall until it has found its ideal spawning-grounds (here again, following the concept of implosion, close to the source, the center).

---

[2])Schauberger created the complicated sounding term, "cycloidal spacially curved motion" or sometimes also "planetary motion" for this, meaning the spiral shaped planetary motion which is the only type of motion that develops, since everything that turns in circles does not move from the spot. Everything that wants to move and develop must execute its movements analogous to the planets.

This example makes it easy to visualize the inner energy that is at work in every flowing motion of the clouds, of the wind and the water. Birds in the air behave much like the trout in the water. This mysterious energy is ready and waiting to be used by human beings in the same way fish and birds do. But there is still a long way to go for that. Viktor Schauberger described his profound feelings for observing nature and his relationship to water in wonderful words that have no parallel in literature:

"Already from earliest childhood it was my deepest wish to understand nature and through this to come closer to the truth I could not find at school or at church. I was repeatedly drawn to the forest where I could watch the flow of water for hours on end without getting tired or irritable. At that time I did not yet know that water is the bearer of life or the source of what we call consciousness. Totally oblivious, I let the water flow past my searching eyes and only years later did I become aware that this running water attracts our consciousness magnetically, takes a piece with it, with a force that is so strong that one loses consciousness for a while and involuntarily falls into a deep sleep. And so, gradually I began to play with these forces in water and I gave up this so-called free consciousness and left it to the water for a while. Little by little this game turned into a very serious matter because I saw that it was possible to release my own consciousness from my body and attach it to the water. When I took it back again, the consciousness borrowed from the water told me things that were often very strange. And so the searcher became a researcher who could send his consciousness on expeditions, so to speak, and this way I found out about things the rest of mankind has missed because they do not know that people are able to send their free consciousness everywhere, even where the seeing eye cannot look.

"This so-called sight practiced with blindfolded eyes finally gave me ties to the secrets of nature which I slowly began to recognize and understand in their own fabric. And in due course it became clear to me that we human beings are used to seeing everything backwards and wrong. The biggest surprise, however, was that we human beings let the most valuable part drain off as useless and from all the great intellectuality that flows through us, we retain only the feces."

The secret of the waterfall is a human secret. Was Viktor Schauberger a person who could see into a time, into a space and into a dimension that is still unknown to us? Did he achieve access to his knowledge via a different kind of vision rather than by way of analysis, experience and research? There are valid arguments for this. Access for which a scientific education might have proven to be an obstacle. Schauberger allowed himself to go into a kind of semi-trance on the banks of a river so that he could suck in knowledge; Johann Grander meditates in his wooden hut or goes to his mine when he "asks questions up there" and then waits for an answer. There are several more prominent witnesses who tell of similar methods that summon their infinite strength, their wonderful supernatural art from a realm to which only very few people have access.

Herbert Pietschmann, a constructive critic of traditional natural science quotes in his work, "Das Ende des naturwissenschaftlichen Zeitalters" (tr. The End of the Age of Natural Science; Weitbrecht-Verlag 1995) a conversation between Johannes Brahms, a violinist and a music critic:

"In the course of a conversation between Johannes Brahms, the violinist and music correspondent, Arthur Abell, and the violin virtuoso, Joseph Joachim, Brahms reveals his secret of how he went about the business of composing, spurred on by spiritual powers within himself and enlightened by the spirit of the Almighty itself. Brahms kept returning to the subject of Beethoven and how he came into contact with higher powers when he composed. Very few people have achieved this ability and that is why there are so few great composers and creative intellects in all the areas of human endeavour. I contemplate all of that, said Brahms, before I start composing. This is the first step. When I feel the urge inside, I turn directly to my Creator first of all and ask him the three most important questions of our lives on this earth: Where from – Why – Where to! Immediately afterwards I feel vibrations that go all through me. They are the spirit that enlightens the inner powers of the soul, and in this state of ecstasy I see clearly that which is obscure in my usual mood; then I feel able to let myself be inspired from above, like Beethoven. Above all, in these moments I become aware of the immense importance of the revelation of Jesus: 'I am one with the Father!' These vibrations assume the shape of certain intellectual pictures as soon as I have formulated my wish and my decision as to what I want, that is, to be inspired to compose something that uplifts and benefits mankind – something of permanent value. Ideas flow toward me immediately, directly from God; I not only see specific themes in front of my mind's eye, I also see the right form in which they are clothed, the harmonies and the orchestration. Measure for measure, the finished work is revealed to me when I find myself in this rare, inspired mood: ... I have to be in a semi-trance to achieve such results – a state in which conscious thinking is momentarily without a master and the sub-conscious rules, since it is through this, as a part of the Almighty, that inspiration occurs. At the same time I have to be careful that I do not lose consciousness altogether, because the ideas would disappear."

When Joachim responds with the blunt question why he was not able to receive inspiration like Brahms – he, too, had tried a hand at composing but his works "are ignored more and more and will soon be forgotten," Brahms replied, "It is difficult, if not impossible to find an explanation why one composer is more richly bestowed with inspiration than another, but I can put my finger on a weak place in your past, Joseph – too many offices and honors."

Or what about Anton Bruckner, God's musician, whose stereotype answer to the question where his musical creative powers and his material came from was, "From God!" And in the case of Mozart, biographers have come to the conclusion that his musical knowledge could never have been learned during his short lifetime and that his gigantic volume of compositions could never have been created with the usual method of approach to a masterwork, with trial and error,[3] but only through absolutely perfect, precise, correct, in short superhuman eruptions of infinitely perfect art.

While it is not so hard to make it seem likely that great musicians

---

[3] Hartmut Gagelmann, Mozart hat nie gelebt. Eine kritische Bilanz, Verlag Herder 1990

enter dimensions that remain closed to the best of music theorists, since in music, practitioners are more highly regarded than theoreticians, it is the other way around in natural science. Here, "theoreticians" rank as the keepers of absolute knowledge and the "uneducated practitioners" as eccentrics not to be taken seriously. The hierarchy of natural science even refuses to come down from the high horse it placed itself on, when Aunt Amelia's gouty toe provides a far more precise weather forecast than one put together by meteorologists with the help of thousands of computer assisted measurements.

The conventional natural sciences fail to give an answer to one question in particular; namely, why they do not orient their research efforts on the absolute perfection of nature which knows no mistakes, no waste matter, but does know constant return. Why do they try so hard to create and perfect systems which are stubbornly aimed at taming nature, at trying to entice its secrets and rules from it only to start a hopeless and childish experiment they hope will triumph over nature, rather than joining with it for the combined good. Unfortunately, this turns out to be to their own disadvantage and the disadvantage of the whole of mankind even to the point of endangering our existence. Historians of the future will not understand our generation.

As early as 1928, Viktor Schauberger warned of the consequences the fatal path of ruthless exploitation of nature would bring about:

"What couldn't be said about the forest and its life! Unfortunately, my job is to write about its dying. The horrible mistakes should be pointed out to the people who are in a position to give last minute help to the forest that is dying at the hands of people who are foreign to nature. Whenever a person dies, the bells toll. When the forest dies and with it an entire people, not one person lifts a finger. It is known that every death of a people was preceded by the death of a forest. It will take centuries for the forest to recover to the place where it was a few decades ago. The broad masses face this slowly advancing decline in quality with a total lack of understanding. They see forests everywhere and let themselves be deluded by statistics that prove that more cubic meters of solid timber per hectare stock up now than ever before."

The fundamental evil is our way of using fossil and nuclear energy: according to Schauberger's implosion principle, the problem of energy is not how to turn the weight-of-fall of water flowing to the valley or the wind that is generated by the differences in temperature and pressure into kilogram-meters or how to conduct the expanding steam and gases to turbine blades and cylinder pistons, with the result that the enormous input harnesses only a fraction of the actual inherent energy.

The supporters of the implosion theory criticize the fact that today's theory of motion only recognizes the circling motion upon which all of technology is based. The laws of nature, however, arise from a system characterized by the spiral shaped, planetary motion. This is the only way to approach the rules governing the cosmos and the organism earth, and to learn to use them without undermining the order of the cosmos and the earth, the way life-destroying nuclear fission does especially.

Instead of extending and perfecting the existing system of destruction, a different system should be sought, one that does not use up a substance, that does not burn anything, for which no wastes in the form of polluted bodies of water, contaminated air or radioactive ash result. Waste that cannot be discarded or deposited anywhere on earth without remaining a permanent danger to all living things. If the planetary form of motion were to be transferred to technology, the media used for supplying energy – exactly like natural processes – would be improved. Instead of dead waste water, water of excellent quality would be created, like that which rises from a mountain source and instead of smog, healthy air.

Of course, today all of this is still vision and theory, only – who knows of a different way in the long run? Or the other way around: is it not the greatest challenge in human history to pursue a system that is synchronized with the rhythm of nature and therefore has a chance for survival over a period of millions of years? A system that takes people back to being a component of a harmonious evolution, reconciles him with nature again, lets the wounds heal and draws fantastic strength and an entirely new feeling for life from the new union?!

Viktor Schauberger was unswerving – and unfortunately during his time unheard – in his demands for an about-turn. Was it too early, was the pressure in the pot not yet strong enough, is the time right in the meanwhile?

What is it that still makes Viktor Schauberger so important for the generation that will follow ours? Water is something that moves and is yet so final, it is atypical and anomalous, does not follow the laws of nature anyway since it does not have (as it should) the greatest density at zero degrees Celsius, but at plus four degrees. Water is the elixir of life. The heaviest brick of gold dwindles in importance when the life-sustaining sip of water is lacking.

Imagine being a forester during the period between the wars; a man whose salary is barely enough to feed his family properly and from whose pen the following sentences come:

"Safeguarding the secret of water is also a way of ensuring the interest on the capital. Interest only prospers in a deficient economy. When the problem of creating water is solved and when it becomes possible to produce any amount of water in any quality at any desired location, man will be able to cultivate enormous areas of desert land again, the sales value of food and at the same time, the sales value of mechanical power will sink to such a low point that it will not be worth speculating with anymore. The freedom of sustenance and the availability of free mechanical power are such subversive ideas that the whole picture of the world and even all the views of the world will experience a change. Safeguarding the secret of water is therefore capital's greatest capital and for this reason every attempt that serves to make this clear is ruthlessly nipped in the bud."

Viktor Schauberger was an idealistic-holistic thinker, whose visions spread across the world long beyond his own lifetime. He was convinced that physics possessed only a few superficial and formal bits of knowledge about water, that the true knowledge about water had not been seriously touched upon a single time and would not even be recognizable with the unrealistic, formalistic point of view held by the natural sciences.

The natural laws of water were simply not what natural science claimed. Schauberger presented his evidence. The name Viktor

Schauberger is inseparably connected with the construction of timber floating systems. When he saw how men and animals were maltreated to transport timber from the farthest backwoods, he studied water flowing to the valley. He observed how water advances spirally in peculiar snakelike windings, once to the left, and then to the right. From this he concluded that water obtained an undreamed-of boost in energy as a result of this kind of motion through which its load-carrying and towing capacity also increased. Using this as a model, he constructed canals for floating timber, first in the isolated mountains of Austria, then all over Austria under contract with the government and later even outside Europe. Viktor Schauberger also possessed a lot of additional wisdom about transporting timber, gained from his father, who advised him: "Never transport heavy beechwood by day (ed: beechwood has a specific weight of 0.85 – 1.12 and is thus partially heavier than water and therefore its ability to float is limited) but only during nights brightly lit by the moon, since water lit by the sun gets tired and lazy, it rolls up and sleeps, whereas it gets very fresh and lively at night, especially in the moonlight, making it able to carry logs of beech and fir which are heavier than water."

Contrary to all known systems of floating canals, the Schauberger types functioned best with very little water. The logs swerved like the water in snake-like motions towards the valley. He took his father's advice into account insofar as he drained off the water after a while (when it warmed up and became tired) and let in cold fresh ("hard-working") spring water. During the period between the wars millions of cubic meters of timber were transported in canals up to 50 kilometers long to get them from the farthest forests. When he began to see that his knowledge was no longer being used for the natural utilization of the forests but for brutal exploitation, he refused to build any more timber floating canals.

Of course there were people who were envious. Some state officials whose attention had been drawn to the "water miracle", sent him the internationally recognized (then and now) hydrologist, Philipp Forchheimer, who was supposed to refute the charlatan once and for all. In the beginning Forchheimer was determined to do just that. He studied the canals in detail, but with all his formulas, curves and profiles, he did not come the slightest bit closer to the secret of how these canals functioned. According to the established laws of physics, they shouldn't have functioned at all (none of this has changed up to the present). Later attempts, commissioned by the government, to copy Schauberger's timber floating canals failed. The imitating builders did not understand the father of the idea. Forchheimer reacted differently: the old professor developed a liking for the hotheaded eccentric. A fatherly friendship developed between the scientist and the forester. Through his recognition of the Schauberger success, Forchheimer who had been undisputed for decades, got caught in the line of fire between his colleagues at the university. Forchheimer admitted that he was only able to think in formulas and thus for him the phenomenon of the Schauberger method of water utilization was unexplainable. He thought Schauberger thought in a way that no other human being did and this was not compatible with the thought processes of science. In another instance he declared " ... that the day will come when Schauberger's ideas will change our environment".

How deeply the old professor's reflections went is shown in words that had the ring of a legacy: "I am happy that I am already 75 years old. It cannot do me much harm to come out in favor of your ideas. A time will come when they will be widely understood."

Are we getting a bit closer to this time? In any case the avowal made by the great physicist, Max Planck, suits Viktor Schauberger especially well: "... In the first stage, science always fights new ideas, findings that contradict accepted views, and their proponents as well. If these ideas prove not to be completely untenable after all, they are examined by science in the second phase and should they find acceptance, are presented in the third phase as the result of scientific research, and hardly any tribute is paid to the intellectual fathers of such findings."

This form of stealing ideas seems not to have escaped the notice of the renowned teacher and founder of the Vienna Technical Museum, Wilhelm Exner, either. Therefore he summarized the ideas behind the laws of the motion of water and deposited the writing with the Academy of Sciences so that if these "new findings will have established themselves," the simple forester could be proven to be their true creator and discoverer.

The life and work of Viktor Schauberger has only been researched and documented sketchily so far. It can be assumed that a study of Viktor Schauberger's work, an examination of his theories and perhaps an attempt to reconstruct his devices could bring one closer to solving the puzzle of water. For anyone interested, the most important biographical data are as follows:

After the First World War, Schauberger became a forester in the land holdings owned by Prince Schaumburg-Lippe in Upper Austria. That is where he also built the first timber floating canal using the aforementioned principles. After much resistance, the government took notice of Schauberger. Agriculture Minister Rudolf Buchinger wanted to summon him to Vienna. In the presence of Chancellor Ignaz Seipel, a contract providing a high salary was drawn up and was supposed to be submitted to parliament as a special law. High ranking officials intrigued against him and prevented parliament from ratifying the contract. In the end, Schauberger did enter government service, but was never able to develop his ideas freely. He described this period:

"Productive work was not possible. Hundreds of officials were joined in a body to oppose me like the solid wall of a fortress. I irritated these high and highest state officials and even politicians and university professors terribly, just like I had previously done with my secondary school professors. I was invited to a number of governments, spoke with scholars from all over the world. I received very good offers, usually from Jewish industrial circles and their like-minded ministers and prime ministers. Russia made offers through delegates. The English circles of finance nearest to the crown made extremely good offers. Frenchmen, Yugoslavs and Bulgarians came. King Boris invited me to come and see him and the later Rumanian head of state invited me to dine. In short, I could have been a millionaire very quickly if I had dared to take up the cause on such a scale before the idea was completely worked out. An inner voice tells me it is still too early. A time will come when this discovery will help the whole world regain its scientific health. The longer people use the backward impulses of motion, the more dangerous the reactions to them will be.

"Finally, Chancellor Dollfuss offered me the agricultural ministry. I turned it down on the grounds that I was fighting his political structure, the religion of the organized Christian church which, all the same whether it does so consciously or unconsciously, practices the greatest deception and self-deception and is one of the main causes of general economic decline. That is so because the church has covered up the path that leads from the other world to this world and back again to the other world. In other words, the entire economy will have to take the inevitable path downhill because of its senseless teachings from which an enormous piece of work incapable of further development, namely "fire-breathing technology," has sprung.

"Dollfuss never forgot this honest expression of my opinions and I was fired. For a long time I couldn't get a job again and had to live on my savings."

In July, 1934, Schauberger was invited to Berlin by a coffee industrialist named Roselius. When he arrived in Berlin, it turned out that Hitler wanted to talk to him. Hitler showed great interest in his theories and promised him complete support for his research. However, also present at the talks was a ministerial director by the name of Wilhun, with whom Schauberger had had a big fight several months before and who was one of Schauberger's bitterest enemies. After another angry dispute with Wilhun following the conversation with Hitler, Schauberger left Berlin.

In Austria he worked for big construction companies and earned an excellent income.

When the war began, things got tense again for Viktor Schauberger. He made no attempts to hide his dislike for Hitler. "I never could understand why these masses of people acted so crazily. I followed the development closely and knew from the first day on that pushing technical progress of all kinds would end in a catastrophe, the likes of which we've never seen. Unfortunately I made no bones about my firm conviction on this, and the logical consequence was that I have been watched ever since that day, and since late autumn of 1940 every step I take has been followed by the Gestapo. Finally, I

41

was taken from my apartment and subjected to severe questioning. But I was released again, only to be watched even more closely. One day my equipment was confiscated by the OKW [the Supreme Command of the Wehrmacht]. I filed suit against the supreme military authorities. The lawyer Thun-Hohenstein represented me and the OKW had to release the equipment. The expected catastrophe occurred and I barely escaped being executed by the SS in the Mauthausen concentration camp."

He called the devices he was working on "Repulsinen." They were supposed to make it possible to put the "implosion theory" into practice. The model was the trout he had observed in the river. The trout is able to stay in one place despite strong currents and, when threatened, flee straight ahead. This requires a tremendous expenditure of strength, which Schauberger says is created by the spiral-shaped motion (implosion) of the water when it flows through the fish's gills. The outward flowing water is guided into screw-shaped motions around the fish's body. This corresponds to a spiral-shaped motion of the water from outside towards the inside. The speed of the water around the ever thinner body increases, causing an increase in energy that drives the fish against the current with great power.

This power, according to Schauberger, can be utilized for generators of any kind. In politically critical times, such ideas take on special importance. Alois Kokaly, the publisher for many years of the biotechnical series of writings called "Implosion" and Schauberger's spiritual companion, describes the forester's later life:[4]

"In 1942, when I heard from a friend of mine who was a teacher and who had carried on a correspondence with Schauberger saying that the latter wanted to construct a motor that would produce high results without any kind of energy input, I decided to have a look at this man...

"That was in 1943. The war had passed its climax, the end was in view. In the armaments industry there were barely any spare parts

---

[4] The magazine, "Implosion," is published by Kurt Lorck, Windschlägerstrasse 58, D-77652, Offenburg, Germany, and contains extensive information on biotechnology and implosion.

available for worn out or broken machinery. Complicated welding processes had to be used to make them work again. This required qualified workers who had to undergo special training. That's how I came to be at the school for welding techniques in Vienna... When I look back today it was a disastrous situation, since what I saw and heard every evening with Viktor Schauberger during those 14 days destroyed my previous views about everything. To me it seemed Utopian somehow, but who does not respond this way the first few times he hears about the rules of bio-technology or implosion? It wasn't until I was on my way home in the train that it dawned on me the implosion was concerned with energy processes released by certain types of motion under the influence of catalysts. That was the decisive step and the first lesson in my basic course with Viktor Schauberger.

"At the time, Viktor Schauberger was working on a 'flying saucer.' It was supposed to become a space-flight tank that weighs 7 tons and is practically indestructible. The motive power was supposed to have 3/4 HP at 20,000 revolutions per minute. The whole monster could therefore have been driven with a foot pedal if necessary... I drove back to the Ruhr with the sketches and with the help of friends and colleagues everything was ready soon. I was supposed to hand over everything to the Kertl machinery factory when I got back to Vienna with the shipment. The parts were all copper plated and beautiful to look at. The director, who was called immediately, came running, his face bright red, and wanted to throw me out. He showed me a big hole in the factory roof a test device had shot through when it tore away from its anchorage. These tests had since turned into a weapons contract, said the boss, and everything had to be finished at his factory. But when everything was finished, the stuff would be dumped on the sidewalk in front of the factory and Schauberger would have to see how he takes care of it.

"Viktor Schauberger was very happy about the success of the work. He gave me a drawing according to which I was supposed to build a refined water device for myself. That was his thanks for my bringing him valuable machine parts and a lot of tobacco. It wasn't until much later that I realized that all the secrets of implosion lay hidden in this drawing. The war was coming to an end and during the nights of bombing we built this device. I had agreed with Viktor Schauberger to come to Vienna with the finished apparatus and then we would start it up together. But things turned out differently.

"Schauberger had meanwhile joined the paratroopers, then been reclaimed by the SS to build the 'flying saucer.' At the same time, fuel was supposed to be produced in the apparatus we were to build. Carbon and hydrogen were to be combined, using the implosion process. Schauberger succeeded once with this and then never again. The marriage of the elements depends most of all on the range of vibrations in which the process takes place. I was supposed to take the apparatus to an SS barracks in Vienna. I didn't really like the idea, of course, but after a lot hesitating and demands, I drove to Vienna with all the stuff. Vienna was already being bombed at the time... I never saw anything of the apparatus after that. It probably landed in Leonstein, the out-camp for the Mauthausen concentration camp near Linz. A factory was built there where Schauberger worked with Polish and Czech engineers. The end of the war brought all further work there to a stop and the equipment was supposed to have been confiscated by the occupation forces, the Americans.

"I lost sight of Viktor Schauberger in the upheaval after the war. After several attempts through correspondence, I went to Linz on a visit in 1953 and was able to find out about the continuation of bio-technical developments. Viktor Schauberger was working on the construction of a home generator at the time. He foresaw the coming radio-active contamination of the world and wanted to prevent it with a life-affirming kind of energy. He brushed my warnings aside, however, when I said that his undertaking was a dangerous adventure because there were still extremely powerful financial interests at stake.

"I returned to Linz in 1958 on a lecture tour, but Schauberger was already in Bad Ischl then with several Americans who tried to keep him to themselves for understandable reasons. I did succeed in contacting Herr Schauberger, though, and I tried to talk him out of his trip to the USA since I saw through the game very quickly. But he saw this as his last chance because of his age and his illness.

When we said farewell several days later and I turned around to have a last look at him down the long corridor of the Schratt Villa, I saw a completely different figure: that of a dead person. I suddenly had the feeling that I would never see Schauberger again. After just a little more than three months, I held the letter with news of his death in my hand...

"What kind of construction was supposed to replace the old models, though, was something Schauberger never divulged. Did he take his secret with him to the grave? At our last conversation in Bad Ischl shortly before his America adventure, Viktor Schauberger said something to me with bitterness, 'None of you wanted it in Europe, now it will cost you a lot to get it back from America.' Viktor Schauberger's last secret probably lay in the spiral pipes. His last attempt to duplicate this secret was a failure. I am sure he did this to keep it from getting into incompetent hands. But it was this very habit of secretiveness that led him to ruin. That was what gave snoopers with furtive intentions the idea of wresting this last secret from him.

"It had been clear to me for a long time that the heart of the home generator was to be found in the spiral pipes. Viktor Schauberger wanted to patent this system. It was supposed to be a comprehensive patent on the principle of the rolling up motion. Several patent offices refused to accept it though and argued that this principle was not an invention in the sense of the patent law, but a discovery of a natural law."

In 1958, America discovered Viktor Schauberger. A number of scientists and business managers came to see him in Linz where he had been living since the end of the war. The Americans had apparently been interested in Schauberger's theories for some time and they suggested that they carry out an "implosion" project together. With the argument that the possibilities were much greater in the USA, they convinced him to go with them and take all his plans and models, too. After some hesitation, Viktor Schauberger agreed to work in America, accompanied by his son. All the material that had been worked out so far was rushed to Texas and a research team was supposed to start work there right away.

"Then, once in their own country, the project managers' tactics changed. They wanted to force Viktor Schauberger to work for the United States unconditionally and create a military and economic monopoly for them. This was the greatest setback in his life. He refused and insisted on being taken back to Europe immediately, together with his son. Supposedly, they blackmailed him into putting his signature on a document that required him to leave all his models and plans in America and "never again" to work on implosion. Then they were allowed to travel, the father a broken man whose own life's energy left him a few days after the return to his homeland, on September 25, 1958, in Linz." 5)

Whereas Viktor Schauberger, the intellectual and philosophical forerunner of the revolutionary way of looking at water, was never able to achieve practical success, the Tyrolean naturalist, Johann Grander has made a kind of breakthrough during the last few years in the practice of revitalizing water. Goethe's words on the exploration of nature appear to have been written for both Schauberger and Grander: "It is impossible to imagine a really great natural scientist who does not possess the wonderful gift of imagination. I do not mean imagination that goes into vague realms and imagines things that do not exist. I mean instead, a kind of imagination that keeps its feet on real ground and strides with the measuring stick of real and recognized things towards surmised, assumed things. Then may they prove whether these surmised things are also possible and whether they do not come into conflict with other known laws. And imagination such as this requires, of course, a broad and calm mind that has command over a wide view of the living world and its laws."

---

5) There is a great deal more that could be said about Viktor Schauberger.
The biography outline of Olof Alexandersson is expressly pointed out again.
In this book only those aspects of his personality are mentioned that have
a connection to the water puzzle.

Foto Fam. Schauberger

*Countercurrent tests carried out by Viktor Schauberger's son, Walter*

Photo: UVO

*Johann Grander - Naturalist and water revitalizer*

# CHAPTER 3

# The Water "Revitalizer", Johann Grander

As long as man did not hinder the water on earth from pursuing its perfect form of circulation, as long as water could "decide for itself" where and how to bestow its blessings on people, animals and plants, as long as it was not used until it was "ripe" (Schauberger) and reached the surface voluntarily, there was no cause to worry about the quality of water.

Water is indestructible, it changes its state adroitly in perfect communication with the existing temperature of the environment and appears as a liquid, a solid or a gas, according to need. As benevolent and peaceful as water can be, it can also be very persistent in its ability to absorb and dispense pollutants, poisons, viruses and bacteria. One need only think of the plague or other epidemics that have been or are spread by water like a bursting explosion. Water can avenge itself bitterly when man contaminates it. Even interference in a small cycle of water that appears rather uncomplicated on a global scale can bring death and destruction. The tragedy of the African Sahel Zone has almost been forgotten. There "clever" people from the wealthy First World enriched the relatively prosperous tribes of this "developing country" with water pumps. The result: the water was brought from the depths to the surface comparatively quickly. The Sahel inhabitants were able to increase their herds within a very short time, but on the long term the increasingly big herds of cattle and the rapid water consumption destroyed the vegetation and with it, the basic life support for the Sahel population. The man found himself sitting in the same boat of hunger and misery with the animal and plant world around him. The civilized "benefactors" called for donations among their own kind for several years to help the starving people who had been struck with a "catastrophic drought." The circulation of "intelligent" water was sped up so long by people who make claims of being even "more intelligent" than nature that it broke down. The same thing happens today all over the world through the rapid use of coal, oil and natural gas, taken out of their natural cycles without even the best of scientists being able to judge the ultimate consequences with anything close to accuracy.

Today there is an acute need to think about the qualities and capabilities of water. Many natural springs have dried up, water is taken out of the earth, forced into pipes, transported over long distances and kept under high pressure until the opening of a tap releases it. It is after this that the real trouble begins. Water is enriched with all sorts of chemicals, with poisons and heavy metals before it is allowed to re-enter the cycle. The soil, the plant and animal worlds and finally man gets "used" water. Water, that at best has been insufficiently and superficially purified by various filters, sewage purification plants and renewed additions of chemicals, or perhaps only "treated."

In a certain sense it is even understandable that science has not concerned itself sufficiently with the "changes" in water brought about through excessive use by human beings. Naturalists claim that water stores "information," has something like memory that cannot be extinguished by mechanical cleansing procedures like filters or chemical additives. A few scientists already share these thoughts and are looking for concrete proof. One obstacle in the way of a broad analysis could be the subliminal fear of the danger of having a glass-clear mirror held up before human maltreatment of water, a mirror in which all the abuses would be recognizable. It would without doubt be the greatest revelation in the history of mankind to have its sins against nature made visible. May mankind be spared this ordeal for a long time yet, or may the event wait and at least not take place until the relationship between man and water has already started to improve...

At present our daily consumption is dependent for the most part on used, stale, chemically treated, sterilized and pressurized water.

This water that is used so extensively that it barely has a chance to regenerate itself is possibly the biggest time bomb mankind is in the process of preparing for present-day and following generations.

This is also one of the fears at the bottom of the work of the Tyrolean naturalist, Johann Grander. His water philosophy declares, "The element, water, has functions to perform that are necessary to life. It provides all living things with the essential energies and takes away their wastes. It is the provider and at the same time the waste disposal system for all living things. But where does water get its energies from and where does it get rid of the wastes? Primarily, water gets it energy supplies from stone and minerals which resonate in harmony with the planets. In nature, every spring has different energies and a different flavor because the ingredients are different due to the different minerals and therefore produce different vibrations, or information. In nature, everything follows the highest kind of order, a steady rhythm, a constant change. What human beings call waste or garbage, is very nutritious food for nature and other living things. In nature, there is no garbage problem, only an eternal cycle. Water plays the most important role in this. It is a 'living creature' and can therefore transform its own micro-organisms into energies through its motions and windings, or convert its wastes.

"Water needs freedom. Living water seeks out its sources of energy itself. It flows over the earth, inside the earth and makes long loops. All forms of vegetation profit from it. A natural form of irrigation functions perfectly on our earth. Only man has learned to force water into canals, press it through pipes, alter it with chemicals it cannot cope with. It is possible to tell healthy from sick water by the differences in their rushing and splashing."

And how does water react to the moon? "The behavior of water under different influences of the moon can be observed very well. With a waxing moon, water lets the alluvial matter lie and the river bed can fill up with the alluvial deposits. That is why there is a greater danger of flooding after heavy thunderstorms that occur during a waxing moon, because the brook or river lets the alluvial matter lie and therefore it can rise. During a waning moon, water digs deeper into the bed. The bed itself changes constantly at the same time, too. It you pay attention, you can hear in the intensified waterfall how loudly the brook works at its 'digging'."

It is not a theory of miracles the Tyrolean Johann Grander, born in 1930, teaches. For him, his research has a simple self evidence. He feels like a "servant" who is in a position to recognize certain natural processes. His results are far from being miracle cures or some kind of supernatural knowledge.

The only miracle is nature itself, with whom it is time to make peace and establish a harmonious relationship. Damage already done must be repaired as well as possible, even though it does not make sense to treat every bit of damage once it has already been made, but to prevent it at the roots.

Johann Grander ran a filling station for years in Jochberg in Tyrol. In 1974, he canceled his lease, withdrew to nature and made his living by building wooden huts, mostly on high lying pastures. This way he "harmonized" his innate "feeling for nature." In 1989, he fulfilled his dream and acquired the defunct mine, "Kupferplatte" (tr., "Copper Plate"), where silver and copper had been mined up until 1926. There are some springs in this copper mine and their water provides the basis of all of the Grander products.

Johann Grander and his wife have eight children. The whole thing began with an inflamed joint no doctor was able to relieve. From his father who had already experimented with magnetism, Grander inherited knowledge about its effects. He built a magnet massage roller which he used to conquer his own inflammation and then that of some Dutch tourists.

Grander's favorite place to be is his wooden hut, directly in front of his house. It is his "meditation center". Occasionally select visitors are also allowed to go there. He lives very withdrawn and can be described as shy. The hut looks like a laboratory. It used to be his workshop and has all sorts of technical equipment in it, a gigantic light microscope (which enlarges up to 8,000 times) and a comfortable sitting corner. Benjamin Franklin's workshop must also have looked something like this. His appearance is that of a Tyrolean natureboy with a flowing beard and the most cheerful and benevolent eyes in the world. One soon notices that he would much rather be a listener than a talker. He definitely has a charismatic personality, combined with a warmheartedness and absolutely infinite patience for answering questions. For years there have been practically no media reports about his person because basically he refuses to have any contact with journalists. His job, he says, is to seek and to research, and he feels like "only an insignificant servant on this planet." The most beautiful time were the first ten years of his work, since nobody came to see him. He was regarded as a "crackpot," and people left him alone to think and work. It was his wish not to become great, to stay the way he was, to help people, to continue observing nature, to learn and to do something good with his life. Grander is anything but an unrecognized genius who suffers under contempt for his discoveries. Doctors, scientists, naturalists from all over the world come to him and consult with him. All of them are interested in the effects of his "revitalized water".

It took a long time, however, before Hans Grander hit upon water. Originally he only concerned himself with the effects of magnetism. His first knowledge in this area he got from his father who had already experimented with magnetic fields. Grander could not let magnetism alone after that. He built a magnet motor he tried to have patented in 1982. It was a generator in which magnets made of special alloys were hooked up in such a way that they excited each other with accelerating intensification. According to his own evaluation, Grander achieved twice as much power compared with conventional motors.

As long as he was not in the right frequency range, he needed rather a lot of batteries for his experiments. In his efforts to achieve the right kind of circuit for his generator, he developed what he called a "water battery". When he switched on this circuit aided by water, he discovered that the high frequency energy from the magnetic generator could be transferred permanently to the water. How and under what circumstances these high frequencies are carried over to the water is something only he and his immediate descendants know. This "high frequency" water was originally only a by-product of his research work with magnetic fields. Today water research and water revitalization are his main interest. One must not forget that his findings were preceded by more than 20 years of preparatory work. It was a time of endless privations and of course, of setbacks.

The discovery of "revitalized water" gave Hans Grander his breakthrough and brought him success. From the previously mentioned copper mine near his home, he gets water of very high quality from sources that lie 500 meters deep and revitalizes it with his bio-technical devices. Together with his sons, he founded the company, Innutec, which bottles this water and sells it through the marketing organization (UVO).

The process of "revitalizing water" is not so much a great secret of enormous proportions as it is a "natural" process that returns lost energy to water. The most important prerequisite for this is the basic knowledge concerning the way all living things move. Hans Grander explains it the following way:

"Fundamentally, one has to know that freshwater naturally has a positive charge and saltwater a negative charge. When freshwater flows into saltwater, gigantic energies are freed; these energies are responsible for the weather. When the energy paths are disturbed, that is, when the river no longer contains the information, it can lead to increased disorder in the weather, such as a change in temperature distribution and thus to a change in the distribution of precipitation. This is because our weather is primarily influenced by energetic processes and not by mechanical and physiochemical processes, the way meteorologists see it."

According to Hans Grander, everything is a balance between plus and minus, similar to the Chinese yin and yang. However, Hans Grander sees the terms positive and negative without value attributes. In his opinion there has to be both positive and negative to maintain a balance. Negative is not automatically bad and positive not automatically good. The same thing goes for the frequently overworked terms, left-handed rotation (levorotatory) and right-handed rotation (dextrorotatory). Usually it is assumed that clockwise or right-handed rotation is positive and that left-handed or counterclockwise rotation is negative. One must be very cautious with these terms, says Grander, because "The critical factor here again are the three cycles. Let's take the monthly cycle, for example, where a strong right-handed rotation can be observed during the phase of the waxing moon, and in the phase of the waning moon a strong left-handed rotation, although the cycles of the year and the day can also exert an additional influence. In nature, we need the plus and the minus, that is a balance between the two. Therefore we cannot say from the outset that right-handed rotation is good and left-handed rotation is bad. Levorotatory water, for instance, can be very good water."

Thanks to these basically very simple ideas of the naturalist, Johann Grander, many people have been able to maintain or regain their well-being, strength and health by using Grander's revitalized water. What Viktor Schauberger was not able to achieve, Hans Grander appears to have succeeded in doing. A large number of people swear by the revitalization of water according to the Grander system. A lot of positive results are reported by users. Numerous attempts to stop Grander and his development, to make him appear ridiculous, to present him as a charlatan have all been without effect.

In a conversation that took place with friends seated around a table (see photograph, p. 65), he complained that "most of the people today have lost every bit of knowledge about what really happens in nature and what is really important in life." Grander, who is usually cheerful and confident despite all the adversities that confront him, gets very serious when the topic turns to basic matters of nature: "It often hurts when I have to look on and see such a false picture being drawn for people that they become ignorant and blind in respect to nature. And that is why I wish people themselves would start to think about the processes of nature again and through this to learn to respect nature again. Because this knowledge about nature can, for the most part, only come from within themselves."

In his opinion, this "ancient knowledge" has mostly been lost. The reason for this: "Because in times of constant economic growth and constant technical progress people try to convince us that scientific research offers solutions that make observation of the laws of nature superfluous."

"Today," Grander says, "people only see the material things; wherever you look, the only concern left is money. Where is there anything left that can concern itself with nature? Not until we have recognized the perfect interplay and the mutual dependence of the four elements – earth, water, air and fire, the building blocks of all material creation – can we imagine how destructive our interference with nature is and how much it disturbs the balance and the order of things."

Grander also says that the creation of the earth is closely connected with this. In the course of his work and his research, he has come more and more to "God." He does not belong to an organized religion, though, and certainly not to a sect. Above all, he rejects the theory that earth was created as the result of a big bang: "In this, I see among other things, the main problem, the main cause for the bad shape the earth is in today. Because anyone who attributes the creation of the earth to what is more or less a coincidence will most likely find it hard to give nature the respect and consideration that is necessary. But anyone who observes nature intensely can see what perfection lies behind it and will ask the question who created this perfection? This thought has always fascinated me and through this I have come closer to God because he created nature for all of us. Not until man realizes that the earth itself is a living creature will he also be able to see how easily it can be injured."

Injuries to nature begin of course in small ways, in the detail, for example with tapwater that is supplied to consumers via conventional pipelines. According to naturalists, water loses its original energy through friction in the pipes and the straight line of the transport. Friction generates heat; this sets off electrolytic (disintegrating) processes in the water that make the water stale and powerless. In the opinion of naturalists, water is an element of coolness, that can only maintain its own energy axis in correspondingly cool temperatures and meandering motion. The loss of this energy axis and with it the loss of its load-carrying and towing capacity cause mineral and metal particles to lodge on the interior walls of the pipes. This results in incrustations and a narrowing of the passageways that can go so far as to make it necessary to exchange clogged pipes.

An additional negative effect that appears with "raped water" is the loss of natural energy. It was not a coincidence that the ancient Romans built long, open-air water transport systems with a winding construction, using natural materials: wood and natural stone. In short, they tried to give water the chance to get to the consumer from the source using its natural form of motion. This method, known for a long time, is termed bionic (a combination of biology and technology); it is an attempt to solve technical problems according to models provided in the functions of the body's organs (i.e., the shape of the human skull as the ingenious dome shape). If you follow the theory further and come to the conclusion that water transported in pipes over long distances experiences changes, you get closer to the reasoning behind water revitalization. If energy is actually lost in transport, the water is overacidified. That brings up the next question: are these characteristics carried over to people? Can water that in a normal situation has an invigorating effect on the organism lose these characteristics, become practically worthless? A theory that goes even farther says that when water suffers an extremely high loss of energy, it takes the missing energy back from the organism of a human being and that serious damage to health can be caused by this. In any case, a human being cannot live on distilled water for long.

The claim that badly damaged water loses additional vitality through chemical or sterilizing treatment does not seem illogical. Therefore, the idea that energy, or information, can also be returned to water under certain circumstances and technical conditions is all the more fascinating. This is exactly what the theory of water revitalization is based on.

That brings us directly to the question: how does water revitalization work, especially the method developed by Hans Grander? The water revitalization of Hans Grander is a bio-technical process that is supposed to restore lost energy to water. The basic principle is that water is subjected to high frequency vibrations (ca. 100,000 hertz) through magnetism. These vibrations, according to Grander, are information: "One has to differentiate here between positive information, that is life-affirming vibrations, and negative information, that is, life-restricting vibrations. Every person, every living creature, just as every mineral also does, keeps in contact with, that is, resonates together with the cosmos and in turn with its own planets from which it continuously draws energy, changes or refines it and discards the excess."

The most important bearer of information for these vibrations, according to Hans Grander, is water. This makes the importance attached to water and the extent to which all life on earth is bound to water apparent. Genetic information is contained in every seed and in every cell, just as it is in water itself. A seed can be stored for decades in a silo without anything happening. As soon as water is added, it sprouts and starts to grow. It is the information in water that activates the elemental information in the seed."

Photo: Lisi Wiesbauer

# Chapter 4

# Attempts to Explain Revitalized Water

N aturally, explanations or at least attempted explanations for "revitalized water" made by science are of particular interest. Naturalists do not reject science. They do, however, make criticisms of its methods; essentially, these criticisms culminate in two accusations.

First of all, naturalists say that many scientists do not think holistically. They do not see the earth and the universe in its entirety as a pulsating, natural being, but at best as the sum of all things. Secondly, they do not carry out their research in the sense of a partnership with and an emulation of nature, but with the intention of mastering and changing nature. And in the opinion of the naturalists, this cannot help but go wrong; it is a path that is predestined to fail.

Man will never be able to win a test of strength with nature. It is true, he has done preliminary work of demonic proportions in the areas of weapons and genetic engineering where the mastery and control of the consequences are something no one can guarantee anymore. One need only bear in mind that the underground nuclear test explosions carried out by the French on the Mururoa Atoll set the whole planet vibrating to such an extent that it can be registered at all the seismographic stations all over the world. At the very most, man is in a position to impair the very conditions he requires for life on the planet earth or to totally destroy them. But that is blatant suicide and certainly not a victory over nature.

Of course, it is unjust to accuse all scientists uniformly of short-sightedness. There have always been holistic thinkers among them and there still are from time to time. Perhaps the criticism ought to be aimed more at something like a striking readiness to accept the unforeseeable consequences of research uncritically.

On the track of water's secret, we do find clear indications, however, that even science has come a bit closer to this phenomenon. In his research into homeopathy, the French biologist, Jacques Beneviste, has found that "Water has a physical 'memory,' so to speak, so that even when a substance dissolved in the water has been diluted so greatly that the amount is far below the physical presence of corresponding molecules (dilution below the so-called avogadro number) this memory still allows it to acknowledge these molecules biologically."

In plain words, this statement can be regarded more or less as a confirmation of Grander's theory that damaging information from chemical pollutants remains in the structure of the water even after the pollutants have been filtered out mechanically, that the information stays in "the water's memory". According to a report in the magazine "Natur-Wissen", this phenomenon has not only been observed by the biologist Beneviste, but also by American and French physico-chemists.

In this connection, the results of a group of researchers from Milan, the "Cooperativa Nuova", are very interesting. Under the decisive collaboration of the biologist Enza Ciccolo, they examined the quality of the water at places attributed with performing miracles: Fatima, Lourdes, Medjugorje and other "places of manifestation". In each case the oscillations or the frequencies of the water were measured. With all of the "miracle water" samples, seven oscillation frequencies were recorded. They varied in strength, the reason why different effects were to be expected. Especially interesting in this connection is the experiment with the tapwater in Milan and alumina deposited next to the "miracle water" in Medjugorje. Before the tests on the miracle water, no oscillations could be measured in either the tapwater or the alumina. Afterwards in both substances the same seven frequencies as those in the water of Medjugorje were measured. Evidence that the "information" can be transferred without direct contact being made. It had been stored in the equipment during the tests and transferred later. It is also more or less a confirmation of the possibility of information transfer in water revitalization.

Perhaps the research of the Milan group also harbors an explanation for the effect of water on human well-being. In any case, Enza Ciccolo declared: "Our work means that every day we measure the frequencies, the oscillations which enliven living organisms. Every atom, every molecule, every substance has its own oscillation that corresponds to that of a sound and a color. These sounds, colors and vibrations together determine the harmony of health or the disharmony of an illness." She explains her oscillation theory as follows: "With suitable techniques – we work according to the school of energetic medicine which was founded by Prof. Paul Nogier in Lyon – it is possible to examine the state of oscillation of every organ, and from this to evaluate the energetic circumstances and establish an equilibrium of oscillation. With the kind of work we do, we have accounted for the importance water has, that the excellent conductor of every vibration is mother and father of everything that exists." (Original from Domenica del Corriere, Feb. 18, 1988)

The aim of Grander water revitalization is to give water that has been damaged by outside circumstances such as pipe pressure, straight-lined water passages, additions of chemicals and heavy metals its original natural energy and information back again. Damage to water, according to Grander's view, goes hand in hand with a loss of vibrations. With his method of water revitalization, which is based chiefly on different magnetic forces meeting with the "element" of water, he wants to "build it up," to transform it to a higher range of frequencies to balance out this loss of energy and information. The device needed for that, which is made in different sizes to suit the diameter of the pipe and the requirements of the task, consists of a casing made of partially magnetic chromium steel. In the interior of the device there are chambers filled with high-frequency Grander water. The tapwater flowing through the device is put through a spiraling motion that makes it possible to better absorb the high-frequency oscillations. The transfer of the oscillation or information from the high-frequency water to the tapwater flowing through the device is carried out with vibrations, with no input energy and without the two waters mixing together or physical contact taking place. The water molecules of the "stale" tapwater are re-informed and thus revitalized.

The smallest model of the "water revitalization device" is attached directly to the water faucet or installed into the building or apartment water supply pipe. Mounting it is relatively easy and problem-free; the revitalization device is built into the water pipe (see diagram, p. 66).

For industrial use, there are specially constructed large devices. In addition to these devices there is yet another series of small products such as a little flask filled with Grander water to wear as a pendant or the Grander drinking water filled into blue bottles.

The French biologist quoted above, Jacques Beneviste, is not the only biologist who claims that water has a "memory," that one can purify it chemically to the point that none of the previous contaminants or pollutants can be detected any more in chemical analysis, without removing the contaminant information. It is still present and is measurable in physical oscillations, since every substance emits a certain vibration.

The physicist, Wolfgang Ludwig[6]) who acts among other things as an advisor to the World Research Foundation in Los Angeles and who works in close association with Tempel University in Philadelphia also formulated the thesis that water has a memory. He goes into detail by saying that water possesses the faculty to store information that has been impressed upon it previously on a given frequency level and to transfer such information to other systems, such as living organisms. He says he can prove that contaminated water such as we find in many wells today can be purified chemically and freed of bacteria, but it will still possess electromagnetic oscillations in certain wave lengths: these can be traced precisely to the contaminants. Therefore, even after purification, water contains certain signals that can be detrimental or harmful to health.

From this, one can draw the conclusion that in water, even after it

[6]) See LUDWIG, Wolfgang in: Umweltmedizin by Traven Talkenberger, Möwe-Verlag 1991.

Johann Grander in his inventor's hut

Photo: UVO

The "Thought Center" from outside

Photo: Siegbert Lattacher

Philosophizing over beer – Johann Grander and friends:
l. to r., Peter Ortner (UVO), Markus Salvenmoser, Johann Grander, Georg Huber

Photo: UVO

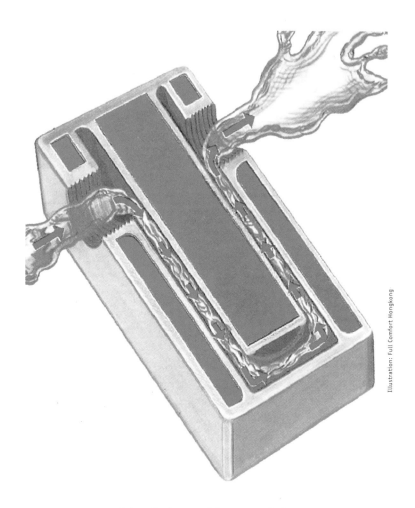

Illustration: Full Comfort Hongkong

Schematic diagram of the water revitalizer
(Blue = water flow; red = Grander concentrate)

Photo: Christiane Gauß

Melanie Lackner today:
no trace of
neurodermatitis

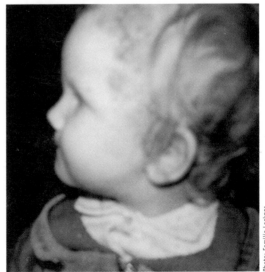

Melanie Lackner:
disfigured by
neurodermatitis

Photo: Familie Lackner

Left: completely wilted lettuce was placed in unrevitalized water - stays limp and wilted. Right: wilted lettuce was placed in tapwater revitalized according to Grander ca. 1/2 to 1 hour - the lettuce is crisp, firm, shiny and long-lasting

Photos: Christine Heideklang

The "Grander leaf" stands upright and is crisp and fresh. The leaf that was placed in unrevitalized water droops down limply with no vitality

Pipe samples from the HTM company. After installation of the water revitalization system the corrosion decreases. The phenomenon cannot be explained with traditional knowledge of physics

Photos: Dipl. Ing. Allertshammer

Photo: Dr. Felsch

This is what the water in the floor heating system looked like. It contained 156 mg of iron per ml (hence the light yellow color). In the bacteriological analysis of the water, Dr. Felsch ascertained a high germ count. 2,500 CFU (colony forming units)/ml in aerobes (germs requiring oxygen) and more than 100,000 CFU/ml in anaerobes (can live without oxygen). This, with a pH value is 10 and a maximum temperature of 52°C in the circulating water.

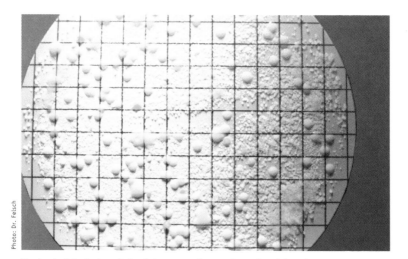

Photo: Dr. Felsch

The bacteriological analysis of the water after 14 days of applying the Grander technology. The picture shows "mother colonies" and in the background countless tiny pinpoints (daughter colonies), which result from the breakdown of the mother colonies.

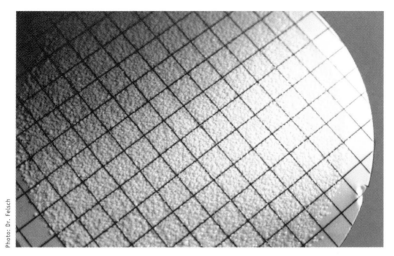

Photo: Dr. Felsch

The water 4 weeks after using the Grander technology.
All the mother colonies have disappeared,
leaving only countless tiny pinpoints.

6 weeks after using the Grander technology the water is
practically germ-free. The fungus, above left in the picture,
did not come from the water, but from an outside source.

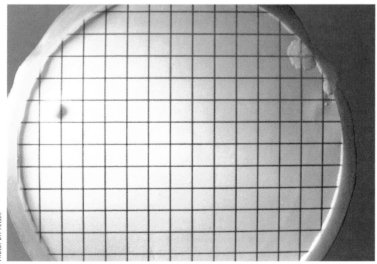

Photo: Dr. Felsch

Photo: Schauberger family

Implosion experiments with water carried out by Viktor Schauberger's son, Walter.

has been physically cleansed, the contaminant information in the form of electromagnetic oscillations is still present in the water molecules. Accordingly, it is not only the chemical substances themselves that can have a damaging effect on the organism if one drinks this water. The unfavorable oscillations can damage, as well.

The question that arises at this point, of course, is: how can we erase this contaminant information? According to Dr. Ludwig, there are a number of possibilities for getting around the problem. It is possible to erase contaminant information by laser and x-ray radiation (which is unfavorable, however, because toxic compounds result), by ultrasonic treatment or according to the processes of nature, namely by putting the water through spiral motion. That brings us back to the "naturally correct" flow of a brook or a river, in which self purification takes place in the screw-shaped, spiral turning of the water mass towards the center (see the observations made by Viktor Schauberger). Measurements have confirmed that the contaminant information, the damaging frequencies, can be erased by the whirling process. If the water has been chemically damaged, however, the damaging frequencies will reappear.

It is interesting the way Prof. Ludwig arrives at the "quality" of water. Measurements are made of the absorption of UV light. "Bad" water absorbs a lot of ultraviolet radiation, "good" water absorbs less, apparently because it needs less. Here one is reminded of the theory supported by both Schauberger and Grander that water takes what it needs.

The question of how oscillations can be transferred is answered in the works of Prof. Ludwig, namely with resonance.

Dr. Ludwig has made a test to prove that electromagnetic oscillations can be transferred by resonance. When a sealed ampoule containing a homeopathic solution is allowed to float in water from which two electrodes protrude, the frequency of the homeopathic solution is transferred to the water through the absolutely watertight ampoule. This experiment can most likely be seen as an analogy to the way water revitalization works.

There seems to be a principle at the bottom of this: an illness, if it is equated with a detrimental frequency, can be treated with the help of a counter frequency. The sick or sickness-instigating information in the organism will then be erased physically by the counter information present in homeopathic medicines, without causing any kind of chemically provable change by the medicine.

Bio-resonance also makes use of this principle. With the help of this form of therapy, it is possible to get rid of harmful substances that have accumulated in the body – probably because of the fact that the body fluids have been given the counter oscillation and thus is stimulated to rid itself of the harmful substance.

Therefore, by exerting electromagnetic influences on water, it is possible not only to erase information from harmful substances, but also to induce positive frequencies.

One of the basic questions connected with water revitalization is therefore, whether it is able to erase the "memory" of the information from harmful substances stored in the water. The answer could be: why not? If higher frequencies are capable of erasing others, a process that occurs automatically in nature, couldn't this also be the case in water revitalization? In fact it could even be a relatively simple and plausible natural explanation for the effect of water revitalization. It is certainly only a matter of time before experiments will establish absolute clarity about this. In any case, it is very interesting to see that physicists and naturalists are arriving at very similar results.

These deliberations should make it easier to approach the next chapter, in which people report on the effects of revitalized water and in which engineers describe experiences for which no explanations exist at the present time.

Photo: Lisi Wiesbauer

75

CHAPTER 5

# Revitalized Water and Health

ealth is by far the most delicate of all the areas connected with water revitalization. Sick people in need are susceptible to "miracles", they grasp at every straw. However, the more one studies revitalized water, the more it loses that mystical, puzzling quality and the more "natural" it becomes. And until it "loses its magic", revitalized water will probably not become something that can be used in a meaningful way. Besides, like so many things, it reacts in a different way in different situations. The Lackner family's experiences described in the first chapter refer to fresh well water that would fulfill Schauberger's requirements for "ripe" water perfectly, that is, water that comes to the earth's surface voluntarily. In addition it has also been revitalized with the Grander process.

Also, repeating reports of personal experiences connected with health in the mass media is somewhat problematical. There is, after all, a danger of awakening false hopes. By no means should these reports lead people not to seek medical attention for their health problems. (There are already a number of doctors, however, who advise their patients to use revitalized water or who definitely take a positive view of the effects and are among those demanding extensive clinical testing.) There is, therefore, a certain risk involved in publishing the following reports. On the other hand the question arises: can one bear the responsibility for withholding reports on personal experiences of positive effects on health derived from using revitalized water?

The examples presented in the following chapter are included to give readers some food for thought. We've made a point of reprinting

77

these reports in as complete and unaltered a form as possible. Their actual or supposed effect is almost certainly connected with a strong will to get well. There is not one single case, however, where there were any detrimental effects. According to the food and drug law, Grander water is pure drinking water.

We explicitly warn against hoping for miracles. Even Hans Grander says that nature in itself is a miracle of perfection, that it repairs, regenerates and corrects many of its parts by itself. But the use of revitalized water is not a miracle cure, and certainly not a form of medication. If the health of the user improves, then this is due exclusively to the effects of activating the body's natural powers of healing or the support for the healing processes in man, animal and plant that results from this activation.

The reports of users' experiences are also to be seen from this point of view. The cases selected here all have something in common: they are all typical in one way or another of the countless reports on the ways revitalized water has improved health. Most of the reports involve skin diseases or ailments connected with the digestive tract. Very often medical treatment was given concurrently, beforehand or afterwards so that frequently a clear-cut delineation of effects cannot be drawn. Only cases signed with full names and authorized by the people involved were used here.

Roland Konecny and Margit Kleinferchner, Wachtelgasse 3, 5020 Salzburg, write in a report dated June 1995 about the following experiences: "Since the beginning of spring 1993, we have been revitalizing all of our water, even the rainwater we collect, with a flexible water revitalization device from Johann Grander. From this time on, we have experienced very pleasant and wonderful changes in different areas and would like to give a brief account of them. Plants in the house and garden are luxuriously green. Since we started giving our plants nothing but revitalized water, we have noticed that they are generally stronger, more resistant, grow faster and bloom more profusely. With our bonsais which we cultivate in unglazed, fine-pored pottery containers we noticed that no salt or calcified deposits built up on the pots anymore. For the purpose of watering the flowers we filled a bathtub that had a lot of rust spots on the bottom with revitalized water. After several days the rust spots started to grow in the water like a fungus. After another few days the rust had dissolved and bare metal could be seen.

"It's not only our plants that feel better, though. We also feel the blessings of revitalized water. Stomach ailments improved considerably after only a short time – I suffered for about 20 years from gastritis, and today I have absolutely no stomach upsets any more. Also, the neurodermatitis, which had spread from the hollow of both knees to an increasingly large area, is completely gone today. I recommended to my mother, who had had trouble with a watery eye for years, that she spray her eye every day with original Grander water and after only a few days later the tearing stopped. Her eyes have been much clearer since then, too. My brother had too little eye fluid for a period of many years. Since his eyes were always too dry, he squinted and blinked constantly and the conjunctiva was always red. Conventional medication brought practically no relief, but since, at our recommendation, he has been spraying his eyes regularly with Grander water, a total recovery has taken place and his eyes are clear again.

Roland Konecny and Margit Kleinferchner

Photo: Christiane Gauß

"In general we feel much better, more well balanced spiritually, mentally and physically. Taking a bath is a pleasure. It does not make us tired anymore, the skin is supple, soft and not dry at all, without bath oils and lotions. Since we have been bathing in revitalized water, we have stopped using oils and soap and so in the summer months we use the bath water afterwards for watering the garden. The laundry is cleaner and softer despite the fact we use 50% less detergent. In the water boiler and the bathtub, the calcified deposits dissolved. Washing the dishes is easier, the grease and food come off much easier even with a minimum dose of mild soap-detergent.

"We could tell about a lot of other wonderful experiences with revitalized water, but would simply like to add our sincerest thanks to Johann Grander in closing, since he has made all of this possible and his knowledge about nature available to all of us. Through him we have learned to appreciate the value of water properly for the first time. Thank you!"

For the sake of being complete, it should be mentioned here that Margit Kleinferchner has been integrated into the UVO marketing organization herself since the summer of 1995. According to her own account, she was determined to do this because she thought her knowledge about water and its use should be spread as widely as possible.

A similar experience was made by Andrea Bangerl from Schärding, Hueb 47. She writes: "For years I had eczema on my fingers and went from one specialist to another. All of them prescribed some kind of ointment, gave me pills and cortisone. My fingers itched and became taut, even got swollen, so that they really hurt. I despaired of ever getting rid of this eczema. Now my fingers look as though I had never had any kind of a problem at all. The eczema has completely disappeared. Even my father noticed right away that something was different about our water. We told him about it then. He had some eczema on his back. His doctor advised him to go to a specialist. Things never got that far because it disappeared with the revitalized water. Both of my little sons have a good time every day in the revitalized water. They really enjoy splashing around in it and splashing each other. Even our drains throughout the whole house are not clogged up any more. In our garden around the house the flowers are more beautiful than ever before, simply because we water them with revitalized water only. These positive experiences have made a great impression on me and I am writing this letter because I would like this apparatus to be recommended to others and for other people to have the same kind of experiences I have had. I hope many people will enjoy having a water revitalization system after me. I wouldn't give up revitalized water for anything in the world. Andrea Bangerl."

In almost all the letters, a wide range of results in the whole area of garden, household, health and general well-being are attributed to revitalized water. The argument that these are placebo effects does not account for better plant growth or a lower consumption of laundry and dish-washing detergents, unless one is inclined to assume that increased plant growth or cleaner laundry and dishes can also be the product of the imagination. (Ecologically, this would even be acceptable since the environment would stand to benefit from the consumption of fewer detergents. It would also be economically worth-

Andrea Bangerl and sons

Photo: Christiane Gauß

while since the installed devices would pay for themselves very quickly with the savings on detergents and other items.)

Some of the experiences with revitalized water listed in a report by the parish cook, Gisela Klement, from the Lamprechtshausen Parish House in Salzburg might very well provoke a few smiles. But shouldn't joy and cheerfulness also be qualities to regard as treasures? "While visiting the Zopf and Hufnagel family in Gahberg we had the experience during a shower that the water seemed to feel unusually creamy and soft on the skin. The Zopf-Hufnagel family attributed this wonderful water to the installation of a water revitalization system. Because of this experience, we ordered a water revitalization device (size 1 inch) for our parish house in Lamprechtshausen. In November, 1992, we had our water softening system, that never worked satisfactorily anyway, disconnected and put the water revitalization system into operation. Shortly after installation, we noticed that deposits kept coming loose and were being washed away. We were able to reduce the laundry detergent to half and the laundry is just as clean and soft. Since using revitalized water, my skin rash has improved tremendously! A friend also comes regularly now to wash his face since his beard stays soft for a week afterwards. Now we only drink tapwater. For all these reasons we recommended water revitalization to the Parish House of St. Johann im Walde in East Tyrol and will recommend this divine invention to others, too. Gisela Klement, Parish Cook, Lamprechtshausen Parish House, Franx-Xaver-Gruber-Strasse 92."

Karin Beutler from Mannheim, Germany, reports on water revitalization:

"After using the water revitalization apparatus for three months, I would like to tell you about my positive experiences. Stabilization of my circulation. Less sensitivity to weather, which I used to suffer from badly. The corns on my feet have disappeared. The callouses on my toes are now minimal, whereas they used to be very disturbingly thick. My body is being purified from inside. Wounds heal quicker. Water boils faster, is softer. When the water runs over them chapped hands become softer, almost as if I'd used hand lotion. Potatoes cooked in our water do not burn as quickly during roasting. It's the same with noodles. Non-greasy dishes shine beautifully and get very clean without detergent. Tea and coffee do not taste as bitter and have a softer flavor and are easier on the stomach. Milk that runs through the device tastes better. Flowers grow faster, are more beautiful. I do not need lotions anymore after bathing, since my skin is not dried out. Taking a bath in this water is very pleasant. Changes in my moods are less frequent and this represents an improvement in the quality of life. I have had rheumatism in my joints for 46 years, and now the periods of pain are shorter. The swelling in the joints does not persist for days anymore. Since I only take homeopathic plant medicines, these work better.

"My feeling for animals has become more intense. They used to be simply creatures for me. Water does not get stale, does not smell bad. In the morning I am not so tired anymore; I feel fit, unlike in earlier days. I rarely have migraines anymore and when I do, they are

Anna Gruber
with granddaughter Verena

Photo: Christiane Gauß

not as bad as before. Negative experiences: none, only positive ones – and I learn of more with every passing day. With sincere thanks to the inventor, Mr. Grander, and friendly greetings – Karin Beutler."

The problem inherent in printing such letters is the simplicity of their construction and probably what is also their downright honesty, indeed they sound like trivial advertisements. One has to take them for what they are: spontaneous expressions in what is usually a euphoric mood.

Anna Gruber from Gmunden, Keramikstrasse 1, recounts the experiences of her granddaughter. "My granddaughter, Verena, nine years old, got a new bedroom in 1992. From this time on, the child which had been so lively was often tired and weak. We sought help at the doctor's. He diagnosed a bad blood count and had my granddaughter admitted to the Vöcklabruck hospital. Diagnosis: divided kidney – backflow into the kidney, bed wetting, frequent vomiting and tiredness were the outward symptoms of her illness, and she had to be operated on (ureter section). Unfortunately Verena's condition did not improve despite great effort on the part of the doctors. They considered using a new method (incision through the navel). Just in the nick of time, through a friend, I got in touch with Herr Kalchgruber from Linz, the advisor from the Environmental Marketing Organization (UVO). He examined the place where Verena sleeps with a dowsing rod. Verena's bed was standing over a water vein. Water revitalization was built into the house and my granddaughter also got a water pendant. Changing the place where she sleeps and the therapy with the revitalized water in the house showed results. After two months, Verena was completely healthy again, lively and cheerful. I can only thank Hans Grander, the inventor of water revitalization, and I myself have already helped many people since then. Revitalized water has become an absolutely indispensable factor for maintaining our health. Not only for sick people, but also as a preventive measure for people who are healthy. It has just now become clear what power there is in this water and what this kind of help means for man, animal and plant in our battered environment."

Because of numerous events during the previous months, Sonja and Hansjörg Schwendinger from Göfis near Feldkirch in Vorarlberg felt the need to report on their experiences with water revitalization in a letter to Hans Grander. "When we had water revitalization built into our house in November 1994, an aunt of ours had just completed her second round of chemotherapy. Her physical and mental state was so bad by this time that we thought chemotherapy would mean her death in a matter of time. That was reason enough for us to confront our aunt with our knowledge of Grander water and to get additional information through our UVO counselor on what else could be done in this situation. This counselor (Ms. König from Lustenau) got in touch with Hans Grander immediately, and he placed a special water mixture at our disposal after about a week. Our aunt swallowed a little shot glass full every morning and evening. A reaction to this special water appeared a mere half an hour after the first time she took it. This took the form of a strong prickling feeling. This occurred only at the places on the left breast where she had been operated several months before. This reaction frightened our aunt greatly at first, but after consulting our adviser Ms. König again, I was able to give her the information that the unpleasant condition would, based on experience, probably return to normal in a few days. In addition she was supposed to drink two liters (or better, even more) of our revitalized water for detoxification, which she did.

"Something astonishing happened: after about a week she not only felt better physically, her depressions also disappeared. In fact just the opposite happened. Suddenly she developed new strength and a new will for life. The reactions to drinking Hans Grander's special water mixture actually affected everything: positive thinking set in suddenly, also interest in healthy nutrition, exercise in the fresh air, being with people who think positively became important to her; she avoided people she felt sorry for. What happened physically was that from this point on her hair loss was reduced to practically nothing, she held herself erect and her skin became rosy again. She continued with chemotherapy but there was an astonishing result: the suffering from the side effects did not last a week to ten days as before. Instead, our aunt was active again on the very next day.

"At this point, we would like to report another interesting incident.

Over New Year's, our aunt stayed with her sister, but she did not take the special water with her. Her mental and physical state worsened so critically that within a very short time her condition was like it had been before she took the Grander water. As a result, she broke off her visit with her sister earlier than planned and wanted to go home immediately since she needed the water. The very day after she took the special water, her condition improved noticeably. After this happened she never interrupted the water therapy again and has thus been able to withstand three more chemotherapy sessions with minor problems. After the special water mixture was used up, she took the 'blue water' (Grander water) and drank revitalized tapwater and to this very day she feels well.

"Our very own personal opinion on these events is that our aunt would probably not have survived chemotherapy very long at her age and in her poor physical and mental state. That is also the reason why the doctors examined her blood count and couldn't make heads or tails of it. At the same time, of course, they were happy that they could list another 'positive' case in their statistics. Naturally, our aunt

Sonja and Hansjörg Schwendinger

Photo: Christiane Gauß

never revealed the fact that she was treating her sickness with energized water herself.

"We would like to add the following sentence at our aunt's very special wish. To her it is clear in any case that she could not pay for this assistance with all the money in the world and that the only thing left she can do is to thank Herr Grander from the bottom of her heart."

An inquiry just before handing in the manuscript revealed that the aunt was enjoying the best of health.

There is a whole file of documents like this. Mention will be made of three additional excerpts from typical letters. Peter Hagen, Viktorsberg 20, 6832 Sulz-Röthis, writes:

"Results since April 1995:

▶ Constantly recurring rheumatic problems have almost disappeared in the meanwhile, or go away with one warm shower or bath (instead of a cortisone injection).

Peter Hagen

Photo: Dir. Hämmerle

▶ Skin problems are beginning to go away and are giving way to pleasant soft feeling skin.

▶ Father-in-law, 84 years old, with heart pace-maker and formerly with a strong feeling of pressure and a full stomach (water accumulation), does not talk about dying anymore. Instead, everyone is astonished by how healthy he looks and how much energy he has.

▶ Incipient cold sores (herpes) go away after a 15-minute treatment with blue water.

▶ We do not need mineral water anymore.

▶ My wife (34 years old) is responding so quickly to the corrective work on her teeth and jaw that the dentist who practices according to the 'holistic method' is surprised herself."

Maria Fussenegger from Dornbirn in Vorarlberg, Riedgasse 50, says she drew new vital energy:

Photo: Dir. Hämmerle

Maria
Fussenegger

"In October 92, I got a new hip joint on the right side. The x-ray showed that my left side is about to have its 'turn', too. In May 95, I was suffering such pain in the left side that I already started thinking about an operation. In July 95, a water revitalization system was built into our apartment building (18 apartments + offices + dental practice). At the suggestion of Ms. König [UVO counselor, ed.note] I did a 'bath cure'. Everyday, I lay down for 1/2 hour in revitalized water. After 3 weeks the pains were gone and since then I have been free of pain. I take walks of up to 2 hours again, of course I do the housekeeping. I am 75 years old and feel like I'm 60. Maria Fussenegger."

Roswitha Fleischhacker, Dorf 35, from Koblach in Vorarlberg, describes her impressions as follows:

"In November 1993, I had cancer of the ovaries, stage IV c. After the operation I had to undergo chemotherapy. Six times at intervals

Roswitha
Fleischhacker

Photo: Dir. Hämmerle

of 3 weeks. I was very sick. Each time I vomited for 3 days. At the suggestion of a good friend, I started drinking Grander water right after the operation. My first success was with digestion. I suffered from constipation. Since I have been drinking this water, I don't need medication any more, my bowels function normally. Just the feeling that I am drinking healthy water now has helped me a lot. It gave me the energy, the hope and the strength to conquer the cancer. Now everything is all right at each check-up. I would like to sincerely thank everyone who has developed and who sells this water. Roswitha Fleischhacker."

The doctor at a health resort in Bad Hall, Dr. Wilhelm Tischler, uses Grander water in his private practice. One of his patients, Josef Weidlinger, Pilgramgasse 8, 4840 Vöcklabruck, reports on the results: "In 1992-93, I was suffering from severe depression, which was thought at the time to be caused by the bad financial state the business was in then. This emotional pressure and the stress could have triggered the brain tumor. I was seeing a neurologist at the time, but this did not alleviate the depression. During October 1993, I started having fantasies and was taken to a mental hospital immediately. Following various examinations the doctors diagnosed a brain tumor. This tumor was already so far advanced that an operation was no longer possible. The location (left, above: the seat of thinking, concentration) was also a deciding factor for the tumor not being operable. I was moved to the ward for head illnesses and prepared for chemotherapy. Fourteen days later, I was transferred to the oncology unit and I had to undergo 7 chemotherapy sessions and, starting in January 1994, 35 radiation treatments. I was not completely conscious during the entire period of treatment. Not until the middle of December was I aware of what my illness was. By then a recession of the tumor could be ascertained.

"The last treatment took place somewhere around June, 1994, and the doctors confirmed then that the tumor was completely gone. In February 1995 I returned to the oncology ward since I had severe nerve pains in my right foot. I had to undergo another 4 chemotherapy treatments because it was thought they would bring about an improvement. My family stopped the treatment then because things did not get better but worse and it was unbearable for everyone concerned.

"An attempt was made then to alleviate the pain with other means, but without success.

"In July 1995, I started the fine-current therapy with energized water (through Grander water revitalization), administered by Gerald Kieninger or by Dr. Wilhelm Tischler. It brought about the desired success. For me the treatments were pleasant and calming and through this my whole sense of well-being was improved. I had a check-up in September 1995 at the oncology ward; to their amazement, the doctors found my condition to be very satisfactory. "

As stated earlier, the list could go on and on. The objective is to attract doctors' attention to these phenomena and enable them to carry on a frank and open-minded discussion on the subject. Meanwhile, a number of doctors have become users of the Grander technology.

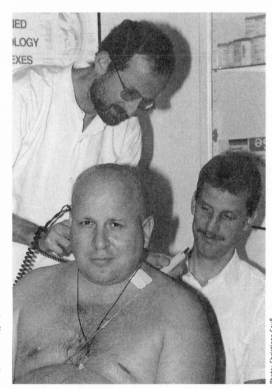

Dr. Wilhelm Tischler with patient, Josef Weidlinger, and fine-current therapist, Gerald Kieninger

Photo: Christiane Gauß

CHAPTER 6

# Effects in Technical Areas

ealth matters tend to be emotionalized to a large degree, and the subjective feelings and experiences in this area are hard to reconstruct. When an illness is past it is almost impossible to determine with absolute certainty what the deciding factors behind the recovery really were (this is just as true of conventional medicine as it is of alternative methods of healing). Technical matters are different. Here, it is possible to make concrete measurements.

There are assuredly a number of reasons why there have been no large scale scientific tests on possible changes in the properties of revitalized water. The most important is probably that the Grander family itself has never really made an effort to obtain scientific certification of the effects of revitalized water. A hardly less important reason is probably that water is chiefly analyzed with the methods used in chemistry and less with those in physics. For that reason measurements made in high frequency ranges of oscillation are only carried out in a few institutes (see Chapter 4).

Besides, the practical use of water revitalization is still relatively young. But when the reports on user experiences become so widespread, then this is the point at which a confrontation between the ideas of naturalists and those of supporters of mechanistic science becomes unavoidable.

The decisive difference – and this is also the big trump card for the naturalists – lies in the fact that the burden of proof will reverse itself automatically. And when the time arrives that the effect can be measured (even if this does not appear in such slick, clean regularity as "exact" science demands), the hunt for causes will begin.

Basically there are two approaches to making technical products mature enough for general use. First of all, by recognizing the cause-effect relationships and then developing products to exploit them; and secondly, by viewing the results and then looking for their causes. The Chinese chose the second option. Since it is well known that the prophet is not hailed in his own country, Johann Grander handed over one of the inventions he holds a European patent for (EP 0389 888 B1), to the Chinese for testing. This is a kind of catalytic converter for internal combustion engines, called Eco-Kat for short, or universal revitalizer. Officially the device provides a "means for reducing fuel consumption and emissions in internal combustion engines and procedures for reducing fuel consumption and emissions in internal combustion engines."

Even though it is absolutely clear to Johann Grander that burning matter for the conversion of energy to achieve mobility is the wrong path to take, he still thinks it is the prime concern at the moment to prevent the remaining oil supplies and the remaining fossil resources in the form of coal and gas from being depleted, and to ensure that the harmful consequences of burning that will continue to haunt us for centuries if not longer are held within limits.

When Johann Grander presented his Eco-Kat in Germany and Austria, the automobile clubs attacked him with accusations of charlatanism and fraud. Although the allegations were made against his person, he never reacted publicly. His opinion was: "I understand these people when they react to my innovations like that; how are they supposed to know?" All the same he hopes that his inventions will one day be recognized. He felt the criticism was a sign that the time was not yet ripe and he stopped pushing for acceptance of the Eco-Kat.

A representative of the state-owned Chinese railway company approached Grander of his own accord. Later it turned out that the Chinese had already tested all possible and impossible kinds of inventions that promised to save fuel and reduce emissions. From one particular report it was obvious that the Chinese had been doing this for years without success. In Grander they thought they had made their find at last. One evaluation says, among other things: "The 'Eco-Kat' (magnetic liquid for optimal fuel combustion), developed by an Austrian naturalist, Mr. J. Grander, is one of the greatest inventions of this century."

With all due sympathy and respect for Johann Grander's work and his inventions – these are big words, and things are not quite that simple. The trial series is still in its infancy; interest in carrying out comparative tests in other countries will probably depend to a large extent on the publication of the Chinese results. But: without thorough checking, without scientific verification or falsification this statement issued by the Chinese state railway company cannot simply be swept aside. China is not a developing country in technical matters, it possesses nuclear bombs and spacecraft. Their ability to measure the fuel consumption and toxic emissions of an internal combustion engine must also be accepted as a given fact.

It is with caution and reservation that the results of a series of tests on the Eco-Kat made by the China Railroad Corporation are presented here extensively and exclusively for the first time outside the company. Dipl. Ing. Dr. Horst Felsch, certainly the best scientific authority on water revitalization, is of the opinion that the Chinese test methods comply absolutely with international standards and are correct. To begin with, a brief description of the Eco-Kat: it is a universal energizer, a device consisting of two half-shells that clap over a hose or a thin pipe. Each of these shells is filled with Grander concentrate and, if the customer so desires, with an anti-freeze additive. The universal energizer is put over the fuel pipe (gasoline or diesel fuel input) and, according to the inventor, influences the fuel's basic characteristics – or revitalizes it. The results are supposed to be: about six percent less consumption and a noticeable lowering of the measurable exhaust emissions.

The China Railroad Corporation operates one of the biggest railway and transport networks in the world, with an annual fuel consumption of 2.16 million tons for the entire rail transportation network. That amounts to 40% of the entire diesel consumption of the whole country. Faced with this high yearly fuel consumption, the

China Railroad Corporation has carried out many tests during the last ten years on various products (made in China and abroad) designed to achieve better fuel results, from an environmental and economical point of view. For example, they tested diesel additives, heating-oil treatments, high-strength magnetic fuel saving systems, a ceramic-magnetic fuel-saving system, and much more. According to a report from the Chinese National Science Research Institute that works on the biggest of the diesel internal combustion engines used by the China Railroad Corporation, none of the aforementioned products yields any beneficial effects to speak of.

Excerpts from the Chinese report follow:

"A few months< ago, the Eco-Kat with its high technical power was subjected to very strict tests by the China Railroad Corporation. The Eco-Kat was installed on a Dong Feng 4 – a medium sized low-temperature combustion locomotive, made by the China Dairen Locomotive Factory. The tests were carried out over a period of three months in Shanghai at the Nasiang Repair Workshop Testing Center. The test results we received were encouraging and extraordinary." Because of the great importance of the statement made by the Chinese Railroad Corporation, a closer look at certain technical details in the test results is made here.

Under the heading "Test Standards" the evaluation says: "The Chinese National Scientific Research Institute uses especially precise computer systems to test the performance of diesel locomotives. Their degree of accuracy is so great that the rate of error is 1 to 1000 per thousand. The test results are in line with national and international standards.

▶ Test procedure:
1. Fasten the locomotive to the test block.
2. Connect the locomotive to the computer and the electronic instruments.
3. For each test, fill 20 kilograms of diesel fuel into the electronic scale pan. Reckon the time in seconds that the locomotive takes to use 5 kg of diesel fuel. This test is to be repeated three times and the average result worked out.
4. Simultaneously, the revolutions per minute (rpm) are to be

tested four times:

a) neutral,

b) 700 rpm,

c) 815 rpm.

▶ Test results:

Six weeks after the installation of the Eco-Kat a comparison of consumption before and after installation is made because the average achieved during the 12 tests shows a diesel saving of 6%.

"According to the inventor and test results from various European countries, it is estimated that after four to six months following installation of the system, its performance stabilizes on a long-term basis. Herewith enclosed is the work report for the DF 4-1358 locomotive installed with the Eco-Kat for two and a half months: The computer results show a conformity with the statistical data of the railway and this is most encouraging.

▶ The main points are:

1. Reduced fuel consumption with higher performance

2. Improved emissions, for example, no visible gray exhaust cloud

3. Increased performance of the turbo-charger, presumably because the carbon deposits were eliminated.

▶ "We have already received an approval from the office in Shanghai; it reads:

1. Continuation of the observations and the tests. Compilation of an analytic report on use of the diesel engine for 180 days following installation of the Eco-Kat, also next May at its annual overhaul.

2. Preparation of medium size tests on 50 to 100 locomotives.

3. Arrangements for reviewing the environmental protection data and – as soon as possible – tests on small diesels and gasoline driven automobiles.

We hope that additional results will be reached that can speed up the introduction of this high-technology product."

▶ Another report reads as follows:

"The senior engineer of the diesel internal combustion engine research department of the China Railroad Corporation, which has

40 years of experience in the maintenance and construction of loco-motives, and the locomotive maintenance engineer have both come to the following conclusion after the six-week test with the Eco-Kat:

1. Simple installation, easy and practical, no filtration or connections to electric current.
2. High fuel savings, very consistent performance.
3. Extremely supportive of environmental protection. Capable of getting rid of up to 90% of the hydrocarbons and other harmful gases.
4. The combustion temperature is reduced and the performance increased by 2%.
5. Brings about removal of deposits in the hoses and leads, thus extended the life of the engine parts.
6. Strongly reduces the use of chemical cleaning agents and spare parts.
7. Once installed there is no further maintenance necessary. The system can be installed on other engines repeatedly.
8. Absolutely no disturbance of the normal operation of the locomotives and other maintenance work."

This evaluation, issued by no less than an official institution of one of the biggest countries in the world, provided Johann Grander and his marketing organization belated satisfaction after the failure to establish the Eco-Kat in the German-speaking world. Seen in this light, the UVO internal memorandum prescribing the way the evaluation was to be regarded by the employees, is rather engaging. Among other things, it says: "Savings of fuel amounting to about 5% are, seen statistically, not very significant. For that reason, we will not use this evaluation to speak of general fuel saving capability. The installation of the universal energizer should not primarily be under-taken to save fuel, but because of the clearly improved exhaust emission levels."

The extremely cautious and defensive attitude of the marketing organization appears to be influenced by Johann Grander's modest basic attitude. Again and again, he says that when the time is ripe for them, inventions and knowledge cannot be held back.

One of the first people in Europe to concern himself with the effects of water revitalization in technical areas is the business manager of Prolab GesmbH in Stuttgart, Beilstein, Buchenstrasse 1, the engineer Franz Geisberger. It is well known that photographic laboratories spend a lot of money on chemicals. Mr. Geisberger tells of his experiences after installing a water revitalization system: "Because of the high temperatures, our film developing machine for color photo paper showed an increased amount of slime algae growth and an increase in deposits from the minerals dissolved in the water. The machine had to be cleaned twice a day so that the paper would not get dirty or get stuck. Without saying anything, we had a water revitalization system built in, and after about two weeks I asked the department head whether his people had noticed anything. He said they'd only had to clean the machine once a week. Previously, in developing high gloss pictures, they could see 'telephone wires' when they looked at the pictures at an angle. That pointed to a soiled machine. Today we have solved the problem. We have also saved at least 200 hours in cleaning work per week. There are no more scratches visible on the developed high gloss pictures, and pictures do not get stuck in the machine any more. By not having to use the ion-exchanger decalcifying system, we save hundreds of kilograms of ion-exchanger salts and hundreds of liters of dosing liquid."

After these successes, Engineer Geisberger was determined to use his energies to bring about a breakthrough for the Grander technology in Germany, too. In a lengthy conversation, Geisberger also said there was a phase each spring and each autumn when he thought he noticed a temporary let up in the effect. He attributed this to fluctuations in the earth's magnetism. This is mentioned for the sake of completeness.

Geisberger is especially fascinated, however, with the effect on his private swimming pool: "About one and a half years ago, we had an ion-exchange decalcifying system built in. Since our water was very hard, we had a lot of calcium carbonate deposits on the edge of the pool. Another problem was the constant carbon dioxide reduction and in order to get the high alkaline level down, we had to add acid to the water. And besides, chlorine to disinfect. Because of these two additions, we had an ongoing reaction between acid and alkaline substances, plus the high amount of salts in the water which again caused skin rashes and redness. So we decided to build in water revitalization. A peculiar phenomenon that took place right afterwards was that the chlorine and calcium carbonate deposits loosened themselves from the foil. The minerals that make the water hard stayed in solution and did not make deposits anywhere. Even in the hot whirlpool, the rings of mineral deposits could just be wiped away. But the most important thing is the revitalization of the water. The spiral magnetism has a very strongly right-handed rotation, the polarization of the North-South axis has a very vitalizing effect on humans and plants. Even people with rheumatic and arthritic ailments feel noticeably better because of the energized water. Only five minutes in the water and you feel reborn.

"I poured two shot glasses of hot-water concentrate into the pool and the next morning I went to the heating room in the cellar and noticed that the furnace had turned itself off. Before that, we had big problems and had to let the furnace burn 24 hours a day because we heated the pool with it, too. The heat exchanger in the swimming pool must have conveyed the information to the hot water circuit through an exchange of vibrations. I thought that was the case because I had talked to Hans Grander about this beforehand. I also noticed that the water was 2 degrees warmer than before and needed about 30% less heat input than before. The water is pleasantly warm, you can feel an inner warmth and that is a tremendous effect. Not only the reduction of chemicals. It's not possible to avoid adding disinfectants to the pool altogether, but compared with earlier, the pool water does not smell like chlorine and no one gets reddened conjunctiva in their eyes anymore. The microbiology is fine and the water takes only as much disinfectant for itself as it needs. I was also able to get the pH minus down, too, since the energized water maintains the carbon dioxide level and the natural acid protection is preserved."

There are hundreds of reports about savings of chlorine and other chemicals in swimming pools. A large-scale scientific test investigating this frequently claimed saving on chemicals should actually be fairly easy to carry out. It would be highly desirable, even if the chemicals industry were to run a test in at attempt to try to refute the argument. Every dispute is welcome.

It would be no less interesting to have measurements taken of the changes in the amount of energy required to warm the water, that is, of the amount of energy saved, if any. Energy savings are another claim that repeatedly appears in user reports, but that has never been reconstructed in a controlled field test.

The results of water revitalization experienced by the Napoli-Casali company described in the first chapter are by no means unique. A number of big Austrian companies, including the subsidiary of a big multinational automobile maker and that of a big brewery, are testing the use of industrial water energizers. The Eternit plant confirms that after installing a water revitalization system, the calcified deposits in the heat exchangers of the heating system are as good as gone. Some of the final results are still not complete, partly because it is difficult to quantify them precisely. In all the cases, however, the users are convinced of a positive effect. One example is provided by a technical expertise compiled by a recognized tester of industrial materials, Wolfgang Allertshammer. He examined the pipe system of the company HTM Tyrolia GesmbH in Schwechat near Vienna, Tyroliaplatz 1. It is a firm which works in three shifts around the clock manufacturing sporting goods and has a very high technical reputation internationally. The precisely documented results are summarized in a 12-page report.

The test involved the circulating cooling water used for cooling plastic injection molding equipment. The reason: only nine months after being installed, the circuit developed leaks caused by corrosion and had to be completely renewed. The engineer Mr. Allertshammer, an officially accredited legal expert, established that the cause was a "microbiologically induced corrosion of the pipes". The expertise is repeated here in as much detail as possible, despite its length, to make it possible to reconstruct the test-situation and to document the importance of this work. After all, a recognized specialist confirms here the effects of water revitalization.

"The plastic mold injection equipment belonging to the client had been cooled over a longer period with the flow of well water available locally. In order to increase capacity, a partially open circulating system was installed in 1992 by the company of Ing. Liebl GesmbH, in which cooling took place via a secondary circuit with cooling towers. The cooling procedure of the cooling towers was conceived so that the system could operate as a closed circuit at outside temperatures of up to 21 degrees Celsius. At higher temperatures, fresh well water is fed into the system for additional cooling, and a corresponding amount of warmed water drained off the system. As a result, this system operates with a combination of flow cooling and open circulation.

"By mid 1993, after about nine months of operation, it was observed that holes caused by corrosion had formed at a number of places in the circulation system. After being examined by the TÜV in Vienna and the Central School for Welding Techniques in Vienna, the circulating system was renovated by the company Ing. Heinz Liebl GesmbH in August l993. At first the cause of the damage was thought to be faulty workmanship in regards to the welding seams on the pipes. In October 1993, the undersigned was called upon to act as a legal expert for the judicial preservation of evidence.

"The undersigned ascertained the cause of damage to be microbiologically induced corrosion. The microbe accumulation in the system was made possible by the long duration and the high temperature of the water in the circulating system. A microbiological water analysis which was made immediately confirms the findings. Because of the results, the undersigned suggested immediate treatment of the cooling water with a microbicide and carried out the same at the beginning of November, 1993.

"Normally the accumulation of microbes in circulating water systems is prevented by chemical conditioning and the addition of microbicides. This manner of procedure, however, is only possible in closed circuit systems since conditioning of a through-flowing system is not practicable due to the high cost and the lasting wastewater burden. Because of this, a change in the construction of the system would have been necessary. The advantages of the original concept, however, would have been lost. At the suggestion of Engineer Heinz Liebl, a so-called 'water revitalization' device was built into the water circulation system, after a viewing of the Manner-Napoli AG company showed proof that this system functions. The installation of such a system into the client's water circulating system followed in 1993. According to information given by the chemicals supplier, no microbicide content could be detected in the water at this time, since water had flowed through the system several times in the meanwhile.

"The undersigned had already been commissioned by the company Ing. Liebl GesmbH to oversee the execution of the corrective measures. At this time, a removable piece of pipe was built into the circulation system to make it possible to keep a constant watch on the state of corrosion. In addition, frequent water samples were removed for analysis. An effect produced by water revitalization was apparently extant, but a slight presence of microbiological growth was still detectable.

"In the summer months the cooling system had to be run with partial through-flow procedure. In doing so, oxygen-saturated fresh water entered the circuit, a situation that can cause the speed of corrosion to accelerate. The suggestion was therefore made to install a new and stronger water revitalization device that had been developed in the meanwhile. At the recommendation of the undersigned, the device which had been built into the cooling system was moved to the well and drinking water system where it was installed when the newly developed device ['water conditioning' = the term for the water revitalization apparatus made for large-scale industrial use] was built into the cooling circulation system at the beginning of July, 1994.

"On July 12, 1994, an inspection took place of a leak which appeared at the end of the pipeline. A relatively similar kind of damage was also detected at the other end of the line. It was possible to determine that these particular pipes of a smaller diameter had been built into the existing circulation system as an extension to it, about two and a half months before the renovation of the first system. Because of this short life-span, these pipes were not exchanged during the renovation of the second water circulation system which had the same construction. The damage to these pipes can therefore be attributed precisely to the corrosion damage of the first water circulation system.

"Due to the summer pause, a flange connection could be built into a main line DN 76 of the circuit on July 23, 1994. The installation of an adapter with a ball valve was supposed to make it possible to take frequent measurements of the free corrosion potential in the adjacent pipe.

"The microbiological analysis confirmed that the circulating water was totally microbe-infected. Using standard tests with cultures, it was possible to determine the total bacteria count; sporogenous germs, putrefactive bacteria, sulfate reduced bacteria, sulfite reduced germs and sulfite reducing spore producers, so-called clostridiums were found. Above all, the last three types of germs are known to be able to influence the corrosion behavior of materials. In addition to the microbiological test results, the chemical test results should also be mentioned: the water possesses a high conductivity and is therefore a good electrolyte. The pH value of 7.5 is a bit too low for water in a circulating system, especially when one takes a chloride content of 56 mg/liter and a sulfate content of 76 mg/liter into account. The damage that appeared in the first circulation system is therefore understandable to a specialist.

"Upon the installation of the water revitalization device another analysis was made on December 13, 1993. Due to the single addition of a microbicide at the beginning of November 1993, the sulfate reducing germs, sulfite reducing germs and sulfite reducing spore producers were no longer detectable. It is conspicuous, however, that a noticeably higher sulfate level is found, with 170 mg/l compared with the previous analysis. According to analyses made by the chemicals supplier, there is no more microbicide detectable in the water at this time.

"On March 2, 1994, during an examination, a water sample is taken to check on the effects of the water revitalization system. In addition to a sample from the circulating water, a sample is also taken of the deposit (which was easily scratched off) on the interior surface of the piece of corroded metal used as a control sample. For this purpose, the loose parts of the deposits are washed off with some water from the circulating system and collected. In the microbiological examination of both of the samples, the search for sulfate

Photo: Felsch family

Dr. Horst Felsch

Photo: Dr. Felsch

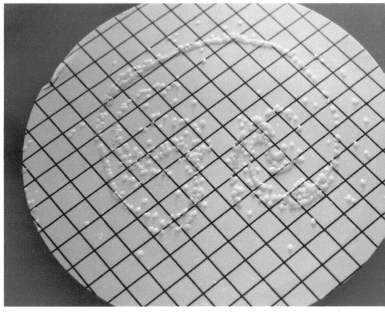

In the bacterial examination of the filler water from Grander
revitalization devices, Dr. Felsch got this totally surprising symmetry of
microorganisms. It looks as though two spirals turn in opposite
directions. The yellowish dots are microbiological colonies. The
membrane filter impermeable to bacteria has a grid to make counting
easier. The red background shows that Dr. Felsch has used a Columbia
agar which contains sheep´s blood. This is to ensure that as many
germs as possible contained in the liquid multiply.

As a comparison to the adjacent photograph, this membrane filter shows the usual type of distribution of the colonies of bacteria in bacteriological cultures. There is no regularity recognizable whatsoever. The colonies are distributed randomly on the filter surface.

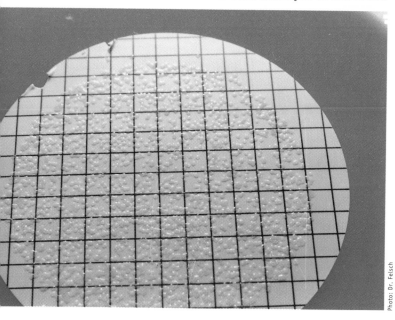

Photo: Dr. Felsch

Photo: Dr. Felsch

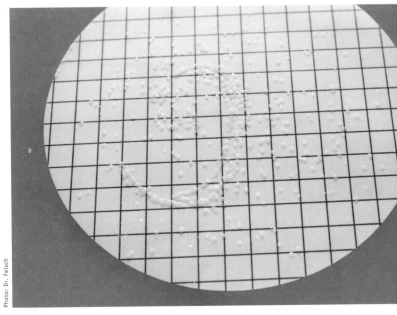

In the attempt to repeat the result showed in photograph no. 1
(p. 138), Dr. Felsch got this arrangement. The beginning of a
spiral is seen in the center, but the second rotor is missing.
Outside this arrangement, the microorganisms are
distributed haphazardly. Since the reproducibility of the
results was incomplete, Dr. Felsch turned to the phenomenon
of pinpoint formation and achieved the reproducibility
of results demanded by science.

In the bacteriological examination of revitalized drinking water, Dr. Felsch repeatedly and reproducibly gets results in which, in addition to the so-called mother colonies (such as the big colony in the upper part of the picture), innumerable small colonies or pinpoints also formed. This photograph shows the relationship between the size of the mother colonies and the pinpoints.

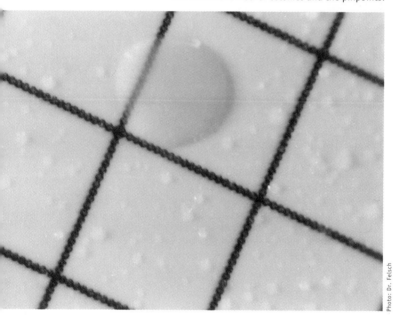

Photo: Dr. Felsch

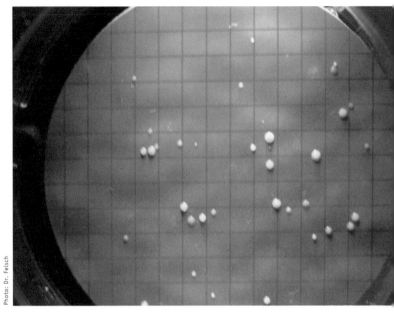

Photo: Dr. Felsch

The photograph shows the result of a
bacteriological analysis of drinking water that has
not been revitalized. There are 22 colony forming
units, mostly opaque, one of them yellowish. This
drinking water has good quality, bacteriologically
speaking, since the index according to the Austrian
food law is 100 CFU/ml at 22° culture temperature.

3 weeks after installing a water revitalization system, the same water supply as that in the previous picture was tested again. After 48 hours of culture at 22°C, this sample of pinpoint formation resulted. One can see innumerable very tiny colonies contained in one milliliter.

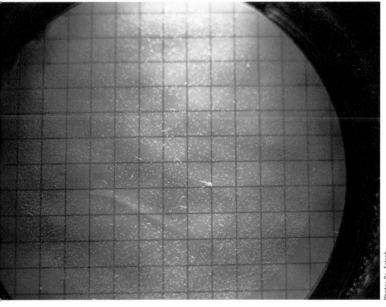

Photo: Dr. Felsch

Photo: Dr. Felsch

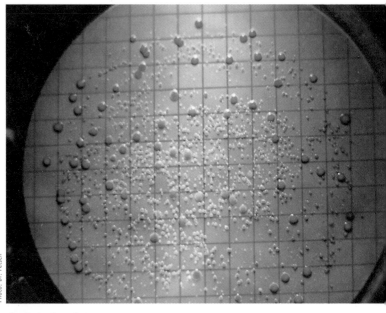

The formation of pinpoints is not a reproduction phenomenon. These have apparently been formed by the splitting up of the mother colonies. This picture clearly shows what has been stated: the colonies dyed red are mother colonies, the tiny ones are pinpoints. The formation of pinpoints has been known for many years to occur in surface water. This effect occurs when water is partially sterilized by UV radiation, or in the transition from the aerobic to the anaerobic phase and also by ultrasonic radiation. In the purest drinking water, the possibility for bacteria to grow back is much smaller. Since there is even less assimilable organic carbon in Grander water than in the springwater it is made from, Dr. Felsch thinks this particular pinpoint formation is not renewed bacteria growth, but the result of big clusters (mother colonies) of bacteria splitting up, and that their attributes for survival are poorer.

reducing germs, sulfite reducing germs and sulfite reducing spore producers were all negative. The total germ count, on the other hand, was higher compared with the previous analysis, with 200 CFU/ml climbing to 500 CFU/ml in sample 1 and 800 CFU/ml in sample 2. A potassium permanganate consumption of 340 mg/l in the chemical analysis of sample 2 taken from the edge deposits, shows that a heavy deposit of organic particles has taken place here. The higher incidence of bacteria formation in the deposit sample can be attributed to the natural, stronger microbiological formation on surfaces. A comparison of the chemical analyses of both samples shows that the pH values of 7.4 and 7.3 are practically the same. The chloride content is also about the same with 38 and 35 ppm in samples 1 and 2 respectively. The sulfate content in both samples is about the same at 182 and 183 mg/l, albeit an unchanged high level. A relatively high ammonia level can be shown in the deposit sample 2, with 0.72 mg/l, which points to putrefaction processes on the walls of the pipe.

"An additional check on bacteria growth took place on June 1, 1994. A microbiological analysis showed an additional increase in the total bacteria count to > 10,000 CBU/ml. The sporogenous germs also climbed to >1,000 CBU/ml. The time of this analysis coincided approximately with the installation of the stronger 'water energizer.'

"The last time samples were taken was on October 21, 1994. The chemical levels in the water are unchanged. This is the first analysis that shows no bacterial putrefaction. The total germ count has sunk to 1,000 CBU/ml, compared with the previous analysis showing 10,000 CBU/ml."

Mr. Allertshammer made three additional checks. These took place on March 2, 1994, on May 30, 1994 and on July 23, 1994.

On March 2, 1994, he found: "The collection of data are based on water and deposit samples. After the renovation and expansion the section for measuring corrosion can be examined on the inside. According to information given by the engineer Mr. Liebl at the time of the installation of the pieces to be used for measuring corrosion, voluminous rust and calcium carbonate deposits were present [see photograph]. There were also several pustules present. In the course

113

of the current dismantling it can clearly be seen that the voluminous deposits have already been reduced to about 50%."

These results, that is, the 50% reduction of the calcium carbonate and rust deposits can definitely be regarded as a sensation. (Also compare the research of Horst Felsch, see Chapter 9.)

Further in the report: "In the course of additional removal of samples it is noticeable that all of the attached deposits can be easily scratched off with a plastic spatula. This is true of both the original old deposits formed on the pipes and the newly formed deposits in the pipe connections. After cleaning the new welded pipe connections, places showing a dull metallic surface are revealed. Next to them there are also some relatively thin, dark brown to black deposits. By comparison, the loose, easily detached deposits have a rust-brown color. When they are scratched off they reveal a loamy, sandy consistency.

"Next, the bypass-section that belongs to it is opened. Here a practically new pipe that formerly had been filled with circulating water and put under pressure, but had rarely had circulating water flowing through it, is built in. The inner surface is covered with a thin, dull layer of calcium carbonate and rust. In places one can see that this layer is broken open and has come loose by itself. Underneath, thin, dull black deposits can be seen. Again, the deposits present can be removed simply by scraping with a plastic spatula. After parts of the surface are cleaned, a smooth, dark gray surface without any incidence of corrosion appears. There are also areas on the surface that have a shiny metallic appearance. We intentionally did not scratch off the entire surface in order to preserve, at least partially, the presence of what was obviously a biofilm."

Summarizing, one can say: the condition of the interiors of the pipes had improved considerably. This observation could also be made again at the second gathering of findings on May 30, 1994.

When samples were taken on July 23, 1994, sections of pipe were removed and precisely analyzed. After a careful technical check on the pipe sections, Engineer Allertshammer comes to the following conclusion: "The test results show that the expected prevention of microbiologically induced corrosion [editor's remark: rust caused by bacteria] by the 'water energizer' [industrial model] was completely fulfilled."

That means that without adding any chemicals, only by installing Grander technology, the rusting process in the pipes could be stopped from the inside. Once again it should be stressed: without adding any chemicals. The evaluation of these results even surprises the cool-headed engineer. He writes, "Despite a low pH value, high sulfate and chloride content and constant additions of oxygen-saturated water, there are no incidences of corrosion worth mentioning. This result can be regarded as staggering, given the state of classical research on corrosion."

So we see: despite the highly favorable conditions for rust, the actual formation of rust disappeared. According to Allertshammer, that does not comply with the "classical state of corrosion research."

For specialists, another short opinion is repeated here.

Allertshammer: "The result is especially interesting for the particular reason that 'water revitalization' and 'water conditioning' were not installed from the beginning of the installation of the second set of pipes. Therefore an attempt had to be undertaken to make pipes that had already been subjected to three months of damage sound again. This is remarkable because the previous damage was caused by selective appearances of pitted corrosion. In the classical sense, there is no chemical inhibitor for this kind of corrosion, since chemical inhibitors normally cannot reach the anodic areas of corrosion cells. By carrying out measurements of the potential it could be proved, however, that even in the areas where corrosion pustules were already highly developed, the corrosion potential fell to the level of the surrounding area."

In plain words, the effect even extends to places that had already been damaged. In closing, the engineer Mr. Allertshammer makes a recommendation: "The circulating cooling system can therefore continue to operate in its present condition. Since this is, however, an absolutely new technology, it is advisable to have microbiological water analyses made at least once a year and to inspect the adapter visually for corrosion about twice a year."

This expertise and its "staggering" results could be a starting point for a basically new way of thinking for science.

St. Josef's Hospital in the town of Braunau am Inn had a similar experience. The technical administrator gives this account: "Since November 1993, two water revitalizing devices, 2 inches nominal width, have been in use in our drinking water supply system. Since the pipe system in our hospital has many branches, bacteria formation in places where the water does not flow can be expected. A drinking water chlorination using chlorine products approved for human consumption was carried out as a prophylactic measure. In two mid-range sections chlorination took place before activated carbon filtration and after activated carbon filtration. This chlorination resulted in a change in the taste of the drinking water, however.

"By using water revitalization, it was possible to have a chlorine-free water supply. This means that the quality of the drinking water supply is improved. The savings in chemicals will make it possible to amortize the water revitalization system within a short time."

Step by step, water is revealing its secrets. With great patience, we are coming another step closer to a solution of water's puzzle. Water, when it is in full possession of its power, is apparently an important substance that can protect us from the attack of bacteria, at least on metal, perhaps also in other areas. The observations made by engineers so far, however, are only a beginning. Research using cross studies is even less farther along. One of the important questions will be: when and under what conditions will energized water change microbiology? Does the technique function all the time and, if so, to what extent? Can whole lakes be revitalized? Can bacteria in the bodies of human beings and animals be combatted and if so, under what conditions and with what results?

Every question answered raises ten new ones. The drive to know more knows no limits.

Photo: Lisi Wiesbauer

117

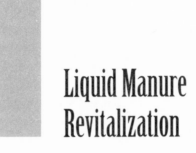

# Liquid Manure Revitalization

O ne of the biggest problems we face now and one which we will have to deal with even more so in the future is maintaining the fertility of our land. The widespread use of artificial fertilizers is continually depleting the soil's substance.

The excessive use of nitrates is ruining the ground water. Plants are often not able to absorb valuable nutrients any more. The soil becomes depleted of its small and smallest living creatures, the billions upon billions of invaluable helpers needed in the organic process of growth and development. Liquid manure, the by-product of animal digestion, used to be the only kind of fertilizer given to our fields. Knowing how to use liquid manure properly is an art mastered by farmers. Put out at the wrong time, it can "burn" the fields and meadows. For that reason, farmers try to distribute fertilizer on the fields immediately before a rainfall so that, combined with water, it can wash its nutrients into the soil.

But liquid manure is not all the same. Its properties and quality depend on the way it is treated and also on its "production conditions". An impoverished soil cannot assimilate nutrients indefinitely, and many valuable nutrients are washed through to the ground water. In the future, only the countries that have healthy soil and that are able to tend and nurture it will live in lasting prosperity. Making our soil healthy will become one of the biggest challenges of the next century.

The problem came about because man tried once again to outwit nature, to force it to produce the greatest possible yields from tiny areas and to create food at the least possible cost. In our economic system, industry enjoys a much higher rank and greater esteem than the production of food does. Correspondingly, industry tends to get its own way and sees to it that food prices are kept artificially low so that people have money left over to buy industrial goods. An entirely different type of thinking goes into the purchase of furniture or an automobile than for buying food. For "more important items", price is not a deciding factor; years of advertising have seen to that. If we do not start showing concern again about what goes into our food, about the conditions under which it is produced and about the worth of a farmer's work, our future, our health and the kinds of lives our children and grandchildren will live will be in serious danger.

Johann Grander emphasizes the fact that his liquid manure revitalizer is not a "universal problem solver" for agriculture. All the same, the liquid manure energizer should be able to "change the entire course of agriculture to favor nature again, so that the cycle can be closed again, at least for a while." However, according to Grander, "liquid manure and water revitalization are only aids that can support this direction; moreover, they can only be brought into harmony with nature if they are pure natural products." The decisive factor is that the animals from which the liquid manure comes should consume as little in the way of medication and chemicals as possible and that the quality of their fodder is all right.

The fact that all over the European Union it is permitted to use fodder made from commercially processed animal carcasses and that it is completely legal to feed cattle – in other words plant-eating ruminants – with these pulverized animal carcasses is evidence of the disgusting dimensions "meat production" has reached. People have apparently forgotten that they themselves are the final destination in the food chain...

What is the "liquid manure energizer" and how does it work? According to the marketing organization, its main function is to activate the microorganisms contained in natural fertilizer. The basic idea behind it is not illogical. Unlike commercial fertilizer, natural fertilizer is made of plants that have been eaten by animals and digested. The recycling of manure is only one phase in a natural cycle.

Instead of adding nitrogen, phosphorous and magnesium, a plant should be built up with nutrients present in its immediate surroundings. There is a prerequisite for this, however. The billions of micro-organisms in the soil have to be able to acquire and supply these nutrients and thus process them for the plants. This "organic fertilizer" promotes the creation of humus so well because it has a high carbon content, and consequently, a high water content as well. Thus, less nitrate washes out of a good humus soil and moisture can be stored in it better.

If we want to regain this equilibrium then we have to keep the following things in mind.

The most important ingredient in animal urine is the so-called urea. Micro-organisms convert this urea into ammonia and carbon dioxide. Ammonia is readily dissolvable in water, carbon dioxide less so. For that reason carbon dioxide is emitted in the form of gas bubbles. So when liquid manure starts to "bubble" it means that the microbiological conversion is taking place. As a result of this process, $CO_2$ gas is freed. The ammonia is partially blocked off by this carbon dioxide so that the liquid manure does not become too alkaline. When this blocking process does not function, the ammonia disperses into the atmosphere. The most obvious characteristic is that the liquid manure starts to smell bad. At the same time, up to 30% of the valuable nitrogen is lost.

The next step is that ammonia is partially converted into nitrate through nitrification. For this, oxygen is needed. Liquid manure revitalization makes it possible for these microbiological processes to take place faster and produce a "neutral" liquid manure. In a well energized liquid manure, a balance between ammonium nitrogen compounds and nitrate nitrogen compounds is established. This results in a neutral pH value, and that in turn guarantees the best possible plant tolerance. That is, nitrate and ammonia should be balanced against each other because of the pH value. Experience has shown that with the help of Grander technology a lot of nitrate nitrogen and little ammonia nitrogen is produced. This guarantees that a minimum of bad odor and a maximum of plant tolerance results.

For observers of nature, there is a relatively simple way to check on whether this balance has been achieved. An earthworm can tolerate a maximum of 100 mg of free ammonia (that is the cause of odor) per liter. If liquid manure with a higher pH value than this is brought out on the fields, the earthworms, whose job it is to keep the soil loose and aerated, crawl in mortal fear to the surface of the soil where they become easy prey for crows and other birds. Liquid manure that is oversaturated with ammonia therefore kills the useful worms. A good liquid manure that is tolerated by plants does not drive a worm from its home.

As mentioned earlier, making a good liquid manure is an art. From time immemorial it has been called the gold of agriculture. But this title is only justified when this natural fertilizer has been handled in compliance with all the rules of agricultural art. Manure and liquid manure should not stink and should not be so "sharp" that they scorch the fields fertilized with them. In order to be able to use the Grander liquid manure energizer really successfully, it is necessary to know certain things beforehand. First of all, one has to make a kind of preliminary diagnosis of the pH value, ammonia and nitrate contents, the color and the overall condition of the liquid manure. The liquid manure energizer is a cylindrical vessel that is filled with energized water. The most recent experiences related by users show that the liquid manure energizer should stay on the surface if possible and not be sunk into the "liquid manure lake". The conditions that produce the best liquid manure revitalization are described in a users' manual:

"But the most important thing is that the effect itself can be utilized completely in most cases, since the nitrified bacteria stay in the top layers of liquid manure that contain oxygen and can be revitalized here immediately. The best grade of liquid manure is characterized by a light to silvery gray color and does not have a noticeable odor. The pH value lies between 6.8 and 7.2, the dry substance content below 6%. The consistency of the liquid manure is pulpy to runny. It runs off a leaf that has been dipped into it. It contains no slimy matter. This kind of liquid manure can be brought out during sunshine without scorching taking place due to ammonia."

How does the best liquid manure work? "Clover and herbs react very strongly to free ammonia. When a liquid fertilizer with too much ammonia is used, these plants disappear and the whole sod becomes species impoverished. Instead, sorrel and other plants with tap roots take over more and more." (Incidentally, these sorrels and other tap root plants can be removed either by hand or through the use of chemicals.)

"The result is a species impoverished sod, characterized by sorrel and tap root plants and a lot of bare spots. Cattle do not like to graze on it. Well-energized liquid manure does not produce these conditions, and above all else, the earthworms stay alive. It is the variety in nature that makes the difference and this also applies to the species in a good sod. Liquid manure that is well aerated and energized by Grander technology also does not contain any slimy substances. In other words, it flows considerably better and its ability to stick to the plants is reduced. The liquid manure runs off the leaf and the grass below and on to the soil much faster and does not coat the sod with a veil of slime. That way cows can graze on the meadow much longer. If there are still residues of liquid manure on the grass, the cow will refuse to eat it." One really cannot hold that against her.

Maria Noll from the Moser-Hof (a grassland farm) in Steingaden-Litzau, Germany, describes her practical experiences with active liquid manure revitalization on her farm. "On the morning of January 22, 1994, the liquid manure energizer was put into the almost full pit. When closed, the pit has a capacity of 260 m3 . On this particular day the cover floating on top of the pit was about 30 cm thick. We tried to make a hole with a shovel in the tough cover to lower the liquid manure energizer through. A week later we saw that there were a lot of bubbles in the top layer. Apparently the liquid manure was already "working" very hard. On February 6, 1994, we had another look in the pit and could see that the liquid manure was very foamy. Another very good thing was that the shovel was now able to sink into the liquid manure pit very easily. Also, a constant gurgling could be heard.

"Since the pit was brimfull by now, liquid manure was brought out to the fields on February 7, 1994, 18 barrels in all. We made the following observations: the pipe for sucking up the liquid manure went into the pit much easier than before, it was not necessary to use any pressure. The manure did not have to be stirred up a single time. During the filling procedure, we even had the impression that the liquid manure became more and more fluid from barrel to barrel. One very positive feature is that energy is saved by not having to stir the manure. Previously, the tractor had to drive the stirring mechanism several hours, depending on the consistency of the liquid manure. The liquid manure did not have an aggressive smell any more and even the jacket that was splashed with liquid manure during the work did not smell as bad as it used to. Besides, the liquid manure was homogenous (like stirred up mashed potatoes). On the fields that were fertilized on February 7 with the treated liquid manure, it can now be seen that the short grass is already very green (a rich green). There is also a great deal more white clover here than on the fields that were not fertilized with treated liquid manure. During the winter, we used to have to wash out the grating in the barn every other day since there were always drainage problems getting the animal excretion from the barn to the pit. After energized liquid manure backed up into the barn towards the end of February, there were no more drainage problems (water savings, too)."

After some time, Maria Noll sent us another report on her experiences with liquid manure revitalization. We would like to reprint excerpts from it to shed even more light on the results obtained by using liquid manure revitalization.

"Since installing the liquid manure energizer on January 22, 1994, there has been practically no tough scum layer. In 1994 we cut the meadows four times altogether (each time the grass was a rich green). Liquid manure brought out while the sun was shining did not cause any scorching on the plants. One cannot do that with normal liquid manure. Only three weeks after the energized liquid manure was brought out, our cows ate the grass with great pleasure. The cows even enjoyed eating knee-high grass. The grass on the treated fields always made a strong, healthy impression (even during long hot spells). We also had very good and pleasant hay (not bristly). The hay felt different than it had before. There is only one drawback: it takes longer to dry. The amount of grass on the treated fields was a good 20% higher than usual. Another extremely positive effect is that earthworms have started to make their homes on the cover of the hole for the liquid manure pit. On one special meadow, we only used commercial fertilizer so that we could make a comparison. On this field, the grasses were not higher than on the other fields fertilized with liquid manure. The variety of plants is also not as wide and the basic grass not as good. If one looks closely, the difference is clear to see. "

Maria Noll's report is not an isolated case. It is, however, a very precisely and clearly formulated description of the results obtained from using revitalized liquid manure.

An organic farmer from Styria, Manfred Taferner, Greith 31, 8820 Neumarkt, can point to similar experiences. Together with the UVO sales manager, Heinz Breuer, and the liquid manure specialist, Willi Köck, he experimented with liquid manure revitalization. At this particular time, the liquid manure was green and smelled strongly of ammonia, a sign that it was not yet "ripe" for use. In other words, the microbiological process of conversion (nitrification) had not taken place yet; presumably, the micro-organisms in this liquid manure had not found optimal conditions for life. A homeopathic "liquid manure starter" was added and the energizing process was begun.

"After a few days, the liquid manure started to 'work', bubbles appeared all over the place. The whole liquid manure became very runny and homogenous. The color changed from green to brown and the froth took on a gray to silvery sheen." After a month, Willi Köck took a sample and Heinz Breuer examined the pH value. The measurement results showed an absolutely neutral value of exactly 7.01. The organic farmer was able to bring out the liquid manure, which had practically no odor, even when the sun was shining without damaging the meadow. The nitrate burden on the ground water is lessened to a considerable degree by such measures.

Most of the user reports on liquid manure revitalization are very recent and refer to the past year. Rose-Marie Gruber, however, can point to three years of experience with liquid manure revitalization on her farm. She says she can see a difference in the quality of the sod: "At this year's harvest, which came rather late because of the long period of rain, we noticed that our hay still looked fresh after two days of drying, but our neighbor's hay that had lain on the fields for exactly the same length of time as ours, looked noticeably worse, even brown, during nice weather. It was impossible not to notice the marked difference in color since their field is next to ours. We attribute this success to the liquid manure revitalized with the "water."

Photo: Lisi Wiesbauer

# Chapter 8

# Lakes, Ponds and Swimming Pools

I s it possible to revitalize ponds, lakes and rivers? Can the information be transferred there, too? According to a first report from the Czech biologist Miroslav Hanke, the Mušov Lakes were "biologically dead" when he found out about Johann Grander in 1991. The three Mušov Lakes lie in the former Czechoslovakia, near the border with Austria at Drasenhofen. Samples of the water were taken to Johann Grander, who then gave the biologist a special water mixture he had prepared. In March 1991, this water mixture was was put into the lake water. A half a year later the water was "alive" again. The fish were not dying anymore and the plants were flourishing. Hans Grander ascertained from one water sample that certain microorganisms that keep the water clean were coming alive.

Of course, the most exciting thing is to be able to experience a "revitalization process" from the very beginning. The opportunity arose in Hall near Admont in Styria. In a little fish pond owned by the Admont Monastery, leased by the retired member of the provincial parliament Richard Kanduth, and cared for by the well known mountain guide, Adi Weissensteiner, a heavy growth of algae the likes of which none of us had ever seen before, developed in the summer of 1995. On July 28, the UVO advisor, Heinz Breuer, installed a water revitalization device in the presence of the author. Using the motor from a heating pump, water from the pond was sucked up, passed through the water energizer and finally pumped back into the pond. In addition, "Grander water" was poured into the pond. At this point, the participants agreed that no matter what results emerged, the findings from the test would be published in this book, even if no effect were to be recognizable at all. At the same time, Heinz Breuer took a water sample which was passed on to Dr. Felsch.

The first reaction was observed the next day by Edith Weissensteiner, the wife of the lake's caretaker. The swans, which normally stayed near the drainage area, came to the place where the water revitalization device was located and did not move away from that spot anymore.

The analysis of the water sample from July 28, 1995, done by Dr. Horst Felsch, revealed the following: "The pond water does not have drinking water quality. The germ count is too high by a factor of 10. The limit at 22°C culture temperature would be 100 CFU (colony forming units), or at 37°C, 10 CFU. The bacteria found in the analysis were primarily different kinds of water pseudomonads. All in all, it amounts to a wild mixture of various kinds of bacteria. The very high bacteria count at 37° is particularly striking. This means that many of the micro-organisms contained in the water have already adapted to body temperature. Even more characteristic than the bacteria themselves is the high algae content. Ascertained were 13 algae units per millimeter."

On September 20, 1995, barely two months after the "revitalization," a new sample was drawn. Even Dr. Felsch was astounded by the test results. His report, compiled on September 28, 1995: "Compared with the sample from July 28, 1995, (before the revitalization) the germ content in the water is a good deal lower." The difference was striking: from 1100 CFU/ml (colony forming units) at 25°C the bacteria count dropped to 22 CFU/ml. (The desired level for fish lies at 100 CFU/ml.) Dr. Felsch comes to the conclusion: "Based on this examination, the fish water has drinking water quality. The number of bacteria was reduced by 95% within two months. The same reduction was seen in algae... The pH climb from the original 7.86 to 8.1 should have favored algae growth – obviously this did not take place."

Dr. Felsch summarizes: "Through revitalization with the help of the Grander technology, the water in the fishpond under discussion improved considerably in regards to its bacteriological quality within

Adi Weissensteiner
serves energized
lake water

Tasting:
Fritz Rauscher,
Heinz Breuer,
Richard Kanduth and
Hans Kronberger

Photos: Christiane Gauß

131

two months. The number of bacteria was reduced by 95%. At the same time the algae were reduced by the same rate. The extremely positive result is something of a surprise even to me, since I have never seen such a reduction of bacteria take place within two months in any comparable situation. "

Naturally, this is only a one dimensional aspect, but surprising results of this kind should at least prompt one to look closer into the possibilities of revitalizing natural bodies of water.

In the market town of Gresten in Lower Austria, the swimming pool superintendent, Reinhard Böcksteiner, secretly built a water revitalization device (size, 2 inches) into the fresh water supply pipe of the public swimming pool. The result: the consumption of chlorine gas went from 800 kilograms during the year 1994 down to 500 kilograms for the next year. The reduction in use of caustic soda was even greater, namely from 540 kilograms during 1994 to 180 kilograms in 1995. The bathers repeatedly asked whether the superintendent was using less chlorine and they praised the quality of the water.

Here it has to be emphasized that the water which was "energized" was not the original pool-full of water since the energizer was built in after the first filling. These results were achieved with water filled in afterwards. That means that even better results are expected for the next season.

In Saarbrücken the "Trimmtreff Viktoria" swimming pool praises the advantages of energized water in an advertising leaflet: "In the new water activating system, powers are at work that for non-specialists seem nothing short of mysterious. Specialists such as Engineer Josef Dörr from Püttling, who installed this system (which is the only one in Germany so far), assure us, however, that everything is on the up and up. In any case, since it has gone operational, there is almost no chlorine odor any more in the swimming hall, indeed the air feels pleasantly fresh and agreeable. There is also a noticeable improvement in the quality of the water. The water in the pool has become very 'soft' and there are far fewer guests with 'red eyes,' that is reddening of the conjunctiva.

"Tests so far show that the water in the swimming pool is practically free of bacteria. The addition of chlorine could be reduced to the legally prescribed lower limit of 0.3 milligrams per liter of water. The water filters also have only half their former load to cope with and this allows for longer intervals between refills. On the whole, the new water activating system has led to a reduction in costs through the savings in water, waste water and energy, all of which will lead to an amortization in four years at the most."

The Saarbrücken swimming pool management also has an explanation for the effect: "The basic physical principle behind this is that strongly magnetized water, which the inventor, Johann Grander from Austria, personally installed at the site in closed containers so that no direct contact takes place, charges the circulating pool water flowing past and compresses it molecularly. Not the least of the results is one that was particularly desired in this case – bacteria die quickly."

If it turns out that a system that can reduce the amount of chemicals in swimming pool water has actually been devised, it would, without question, amount to major ecological progress. Dr. Horst Felsch is on the track of the explanation behind these astonishing observations.

# CHAPTER 9

# The Research of Dr. Felsch

Horst Felsch, duly authorized and officially accredited civil engineer for technical chemistry and publicly authorized legal authority for environmental protection, runs a test laboratory in the Tirolean town of Fieberbrunn. His original task was to examine the Grander water intended for sale for its relevant contents, such as bacteria, nitrates, etc., to guarantee that the water adhered to the strict criteria of the food law. In other words, he performed a purely routine check on hygiene and quality.

With the acquisition of a defunct copper mine in Jochberg near Kitzbühel in Tyrol, the Grander family came into possession of a spring that has its source at a tunnel depth of 500 meters. With this "raw material," the quality requirements for drinking water are easily fulfilled. Most remarkable is that the nitrate content (for which the allowable limit in Austria is still set at 100 mg/l at present) lies at only 2.1 mg/l.

It did not take long for things to happen the way they were bound to. Originally, Dr. Felsch could not make any sense of "revitalized" water, if for no other reason than because of his university training, so he concentrated on the aforementioned formal criteria in cooperation with the institutes of hygiene at the universities of Graz and Vienna. Nevertheless, he very quickly became "curious." The logical question for the natural scientist is: does Grander water have a different energetic structure than normal drinking water, and if so, can it be proven? A tricky question that no one can really pursue officially since science more or less excludes the possibility from the outset.

135

Dr. Felsch started concerning himself with Johann Grander's "revitalized" water in his laboratory. He reports: "I think I was one of the first to take a serious look at the microbiology of Grander water. I carried out routine germ count tests to check the quality. One day I also examined the water that was used to fill the Grander devices because I wanted to see if this water was irreproachable microbiologically. There could have been a danger of prohibited germs getting from this water into the drinking water."

During one of these tests Dr. Felsch made a discovery. Although it was sensational and amazing, no one has been able to repeat it in such a pronounced form again, so that scientifically speaking, it is irrelevant. But it did give cause for thought, and above all, it gave Dr. Felsch the courage to look farther. In all of his 30 years of professional experience up to that moment, he had never experienced such a phenomenon. There is also no other known reference to it in specialized literature. In order to be able to appreciate this "discovery" it is necessary to know about the way a germ count is arrived at. The following is an attempt to explain this in understandable terms.

In order to determine the germ count using the membrane filter method, scientists use membrane filters (diameter 45 millimeters) that are impermeable to bacteria. These filters are made of cellulose derivatives with tiny pores from 0.2 to 0.45 micrometers in size (a micrometer = 1/1,000 millimeter). These pores are so tiny that the bacteria cannot pass through them. The bacteria are caught in the filter while the germ-free water is sucked up through the tiny holes. Then the filters with the bacteria are placed in a nutrient medium and kept at a certain temperature to culture the bacteria, that is, make them grow enough to be visible. In any "normal" water sample, these filtered micro-organisms are distributed unsymmetrically and chaotically on the membrane filter. This was not so in one, albeit only one, sample of Grander filler-water. (Later this phenomenon was visible a second time in a weaker form.)

"In all of my 30 years of professional practice, I have never seen such a thing. I showed the Grander water sample to an electrical engineer. He said he was well acquainted with this formation, since it had the same appearance as iron filings distributed in water and approached with a magnet. Then, too, the iron filings line up with the lines of force in the magnetic field. One rotation center corresponds to the South Pole, the other to the North Pole, and in between there is a charge equilibrium (see photograph, p. 122). For me this was the first scientific indication that Grander water exerts an influence on bacteria. Grander water forces the micro-organisms to depart from their chance distribution and line up with the magnetic field," Dr. Felsch explained in the spring of 1994. And further, "If a scientist like myself is constantly required by his professional duty to view everything objectively and neutrally, then a strikingly unexpected manifestation which is impossible to manipulate, makes him think. And something like this happens if one does scientific work with Grander water over a longer period of time. Up to this point, I had never seen any proof that Grander water really possesses exceptional properties. For natural scientists it is always like this: as long as there is no proof, claims of this kind are viewed with scepticism, and usually very critically."

For specialists, Dr. Felsch has prepared some additional information on this phenomenon. "This unusual distribution would normally be clear proof that powers were at work in the Grander concentrate itself or from outside, that forced the colony forming units (CFU) into this symmetrical formation. But since I could not succeed in repeating this manifestation convincingly, this meant that the scientific proof was not successfully established, either. Several people to whom I showed this photograph were of the opinion that the cosmic constellation on the day of the test was the decisive factor. It was October 6, 1993. I mention this for all those who are more knowledgeable about the constellations than I am. In retrospect, this manifestation was for me an indication that I should look more thoroughly into the properties of Grander water from a bacteriological point of view."

Meanwhile, Dr. Felsch has been concentrating on a different phenomenon that is probably even much more interesting. It might even be the first explanation for the cause of the effects of "revitalized" water. And that, if it can be applied systematically, could possibly mean a revolution in practical chemistry in many, many areas of life. It could be the start of a completely new way of looking at water.

Remember that this research has only been going on for two years. And one must approach the problem with the greatest caution. Any precipitous outbreaks of euphoria or, even worse, an error would create setbacks almost impossible to manage.

Another danger lies in the possibility that mankind could be led into thinking that every kind of water damage can be repaired, so that the need for handling this precious treasure carefully is super-fluous. An erroneous opinion of this kind must be combated from the very beginning.

In December, 1994, Dr. Felsch noticed "peculiar" results from bacteria cultures in "revitalized" water again. He had been commissioned to put together an expertise concerning a corrosion case. A heating system built into the floor of a Tirolean hotel with 200 beds had enormous rust damage in its pipes. The objective report by Dr. Felsch is possibly one of the most sensational discoveries in the attempt to track down the answer to water's puzzle. "The analysis of the water in the pipes showed an iron content of 156 mg/liter and a clearly alkaline pH value of 10! This water had been treated four years before with an alkaline corrosion inhibitor." (See photograph, p. 70)

Dr. Felsch continues: "In the bacteriological examination of the water in the pipes I was able to determine that there was a high instance of bacteria: 2,500 CFU/ml in aerobes (organisms that live only in the presence of oxygen), more than 100,000 CFU/ml in anaerobes (bacteria that can live without the presence of oxygen). This, with a pH-Value of 10 and a maximum temperature in the circulatory system of 52°C!" You see what bacteria are able to withstand.

In plain words, the water was totally loused up. The bacteria ate the contents of the corrosion inhibitor, created products of metabolism and in this way promoted enormous rust formation.

Fourteen days after installing the Grander technology, a definite bacteriological change could be detected: the water quality had unmistakably improved. In order to be absolutely certain and to obtain additional proof, Dr. Felsch had a parallel test run by an external institute. (They are still looking today for the "chemical substance" he used.) In the samples of the water tested there were distinct parent colonies and also some small daughter colonies (pin points) already recognizable (see picture of test, p. 70).

Four weeks after initiating the Grander technology, all the mother colonies had disappeared, disintegrated as it were into daughter colonies (see photograph of the test sample, p. 71). All that was left was a colossal number of pin points. After six weeks of use, the water was practically free of bacteria, as though a miracle had taken place. In the picture (p. 71) there is still one fungus visible, but it did not come from the water itself, it was introduced externally!

What had happened? Dr. Felsch: "Through the use of the Grander technology, all aerobic and anaerobic germs were killed within six weeks. This result was also confirmed by external laboratories."

Scientifically, the question is: "How was it possible to render these already resistant bacteria harmless without adding a disinfecting agent? In the many bacteriological tests made on water treated with Grander technology, I repeatedly detected a change: after more than 48 hours' incubation period, tiny colonies of bacteria form on the plate. The outer shape of these colonies differ from that of the mother colonies (see photographs). If you count these tiny colonies along with the others, it means that the Grander technology causes an increase in bacteria at first. If this water is examined over a long period of time, then one sees that the mother colonies that appeared in the first 48 hours keep getting fewer in number, but there are more and more pin points. After a time, the number of pin points also diminishes, and the result is practically bacteria-free water. This process can be accelerated if – as described previously – the water reaches higher temperatures. At $52°C$ and pH 10, this killing process lasts about six weeks. At room temperature, I could establish proof of practically bacteria-free water after about eight weeks. By analyzing the assimilable organic carbon (AOC), it could be shown that this increase in the number of bacteria was not an increase. The AOC in the Grander water was less than in well water, which indicates that the nutrients available to bacteria were reduced by the use of the Grander technique."

Felsch continues: "An increase in bacteria concurrent with a reduced supply of nutrients is highly improbable! As I see it, the pin points are the result of the mother colonies (which consist of many single bacteria) splitting up into daughter colonies. This splitting up process is a result of the information transfer brought about through the Grander technology. I was able to prove that the daughter colonies have different properties than the mother colonies, such as:

- ▶ they are more sensitive to temperature than the mother colonies
- ▶ they are considerably more sensitive to disinfectants
- ▶ several bacteriological reactions can be accelerated. These altered properties make various kinds of application possible."

So much for Dr. Felsch's first analysis. What happens is that colonies of bacteria split up into tiny colonies that can barely stay alive and that have different properties; they die easily, even without the slightest use of chemical agents.

A scientist is not allowed to speculate, but a lay person can. What happens if germs which cause infections become more sensitive because of the effects of "revitalized" water at 36°C body temperature? Then the body would need only little or no fever to fight it – perhaps even no antibiotics. So far there have been no scientific tests in this direction. The technology is also too young for this. But wouldn't a test on a large scale involving additions of Grander water be interesting? The user testimonies on the effects of "revitalized" water could provide encouragement.

Dr. Felsch summarizes: "Scientific examination of the effectiveness of the Grander technology has produced a wealth of interesting results:

1) Microorganisms subjected to the Grander technology become more sensitive to temperature and to disinfectants (this could be a reference to the frequent claim that less chlorine is needed in swimming pools filled with Grander water), on the other hand, they become more active during certain bacteriological reactions. From this, several important possibilities for application arise that will be investigated in tests planned for the future (liquid manure, compost, sewage treatment plants, etc.).

2) The Grander technology employs neither permanent magnets nor electromagnets.

3) The principle behind the effects of Grander technology has not

yet been completely examined. In any case, no energy is transferred, otherwise the device would have to become ineffective after a certain period of time. Revitalization devices for general use have been made since 1989. I was able to prove conclusively the microbiological effectiveness of one of these prototypes in April of 1995. Apparently information is transferred from the Grander devices, or Grander water, to the flowing medium. This seems to make it possible for the flowing medium's own information to be erased or changed. Information concerning harmful substances in water might possibly even be removed."

The information theory agrees with scientific statements in the book, "Wasser," (ed. tr: "Water") by Ivan Engler (Sommer-Verlag 1991). In particular, I point to the chapter, "Wasser als Informationsträger" (tr: Water as the Carrier of Information) written by Professors Resch and Gutmann from the Technical University in Vienna.

As previously mentioned, the hunt for the answers to water's secret has just begun.

Since August, 1995, the first mineral water to be revitalized according to the Grander method has been available. It is the "Thalheimer Schlossbrunn Heilwasser" from Thalheim an der Mur. This mineral water shows essentially the same properties as revitalized water in heating systems. The mother colony of bacteria disintegrate. The already excellent bacteriological levels of this mineral water were improved even more by revitalization. (See photographs with explanation.)

CHAPTER 10

# Other Observations

In addition to the "big" observations in areas of health, technology and the revitalization of liquid manure, there are also many, many observations on a smaller scale that are perhaps not quite so refined or seem to be highly subjective. Presented by themselves, they would certainly give a false impression. They are included here as an encore, as the dot on the i, to round off the accounts of experiences related earlier. Seen in this light, they are most interesting and quite useful.

The observations made by the couple, Elisabeth and Gerhard Geckeler, Talstrasse 20, D-72532 Gomadingen-Wasserstetten in Germany are particularly fascinating. The Geckelers are so-called Demeter farmers, and as such work strictly along organic lines. For example, they use absolutely no chemicals, no artificial fertilizer and no chemical pesticides or herbicides in cultivating their vegetables. The letter from Mr. and Mrs. Geckeler states:

"We have been running an organic vegetable farm for 21 years on the harsh Swabian Alb. For fourteen years we have had Demeter recognition. We always try to grow and sell products of high quality in harmony with nature. After we heard about the Grander water revitalization process, it seemed the obvious thing for us to do was to have a water revitalization device (1 inch) built into the plumbing system in our house. The installation took place at the end of February 1994. Since then, we have been able to make several observations with living water and would like to report to you about them.

"A small brook runs through our meadow-land. The water comes from a nearby mountain. Several conventional farmers have their fields on this mountain. Through the years, the water in the little brook got more and more unsightly. We had not been able to use this water for our vegetable farm any more for years. Our sheep wouldn't drink any of this water, either. On his visit in February, 1994, Mr. Schoch (UVO adviser) brought 20 liters of living water from his house. He poured the water into this brook. After the water revitalization device was installed in our house, he added another 80 to 100 liters of living water to the brook. We observed that 14 days later, for the first time in years, deer from the forest jumped over the fence and drank water from the brook. Our sheep also started drinking the brook water. In the course of the next few months, an additional 200 liters of living water was poured into the brook. The water had more life, it had more movement, was more dynamic. Despite the hot summer, the healing process continued. Now we have a little brook with water as clear as glass (something that even a number of people in the village have noticed.)

"The water in our water barrel (capacity, 300 liters) in the green house remained clear as glass the whole summer – it did not turn green. There was no visible algae growth.

"We think the water tastes very good. The sheep's coats are very curly and soft. On January 20 three lambs were born – so beautiful and healthy and strong! It is a real joy. In 1994, we had three vegetable harvests. We've never had that before. We also grow several kinds of potted plants for our customers at the open market. It is interesting to note that this year the 'Everlasting Love' was big enough for sale after only 18 days. It used to take four weeks. The flavor of the cucumbers is much stronger and the lettuce heads are much firmer. We have the best cress far and wide. The shells of the eggs from our hens have gotten much harder. The water also seems to agree with the hens. Water revitalization is a good thing. We think it is wonderful that such a thing exists and we are happy to be able to improve the quality of our products even more."

A mere detail, but one that may be interesting to some people, follows. A radiesthetist, in other words someone who masters the use of the dowsing rod, had a water revitalization system built into the water pipes in his apartment at the suggestion of the retired druggist and enthusiastic Grander follower, Ludwig Albinus. Afterwards he tested the water with a dowsing rod. Johann Gustav Görlich from Vienna's 19th district, Budinskygasse 17/8, writes about this in a letter to Mr. Albinus: "In Vienna the quality of the water varies greatly from one district to another because of the inflow from three high mountain sources and the intermittent addition of ground water. Our supply is mostly fed by water from Schöpfl (ed. remark: the highest mountain in the Vienna Woods), which results in a relatively good quality. Our water – radiesthetically tested – has a plus-value of 5, a negative-value of 1. When you stop to think that every negative value point can only be balanced out with three times the plus value, it means 5-(1x3)=2. Our normal water, as it flows from the tap, therefore has a plus-value of 2.

"I measured the water again after installing your device and came to a plus-value of 13 and a negative-value of 0. That means the relationship is 13:2, in other words, the water that was changed by the Grander device is six and a half times better and healthier that the normal water. Given the fact that the water in other parts of the city, especially in the eastern areas, has a much poorer quality, I must say that with your device, an important step forward has been taken in regard to health. (Incidentally, a bath in the changed water cannot be compared with one taken in the usual tap water.)"

This letter may possibly be a treasure trove for radiesthesia researchers. In any case it is included here for the sake of completeness.

The innkeeper, Friedrich Maurer, Ludersdorf 3, 8200 Gleisdorf, has had a water revitalization device operating in his restaurant since March, 1995. He reports:

"In earlier years, we used rather a lot of chemicals (chlorine and pH minus). Since installing the water revitalization equipment our consumption of chemicals has dropped 50%. The water energizing system was built in during March of 1995. The kitchen staff told me that the water was not hot enough at 55 degrees to wash the greasy dishes. Once the water revitalization system had been installed I turned it down to 50 degrees at first and then down to 48 degrees and left it there. A short time later they told me in the kitchen that the water was much too hot and it should be turned down cooler. That was one of the most striking things I noticed after building in the water energizer, namely that compared with the situation before, much less energy is needed to heat the water.

"After the lecture by Mr. Breuer on water revitalization I started thinking things over and told the chambermaid to wash the laundry with 50% less detergent. She did that, but the result was negative, it didn't work. People gave me disapproving looks because I said she should wash the laundry with 50% less detergent. After installing the water energizer it did work, and since then our laundry requires half as much detergent as before. I think that is an enormous saving when you consider how much detergent is used in the restaurant and hotel business. I financed the water revitalization equipment in a year with the savings from using less detergent.

"I have also tried to cut costs in the tavern by telling the service-

Innkeeper
Friedrich Maurer

repair man to regulate the glass washing machine to use 50% less detergent. He had a look at it, was somewhat sceptical and then said that it wouldn't work turned it back the way we had him set it. We then tried it out and it did work and the serviceman returned three times just to convince himself it was really working. All I can say is that it washes just as well as it did before. In the kitchen we were also able to cut down on the amount of dish washing detergents and various cleansers used.

"The whole thing is certainly not only a source of savings for the business, it is also a gigantic success for the environment. I am also quite sure one of the most important basic ideas behind water revitalization is that one does not only reap personal benefits. The environment also profits from it. At the same time we have seen for ourselves that the water is much softer than before, much more pleasant on the skin and one does not need so much skin cream. My wife, especially, used to have to rub cream into her skin regularly after a bath or shower."

Angela Howecker from Linz suffered such serious injuries in a car accident that in 1990 she had to decide whether to go into early retirement. Her husband, Robert, whose job has to do with sewage treatment plants, got a water revitalization device. Mrs. Howecker talks about the effects:

"My first contact with energized water was very pleasant. It did me good and I was not tired after taking a bath, either. It had a very invigorating effect. After that I took baths in it regularly, in the morning and in the evening, sometimes even at night, without adding anything to the water. In addition, I also drank a lot of water. As a result of the rear-end collision, I suffered from a spinal injury which caused me a lot of pain and problems with movement. After about 14 days I gradually felt I had more strength and after four weeks I could begin to move better and better. As a sales person, I'm on my feet a lot and by early afternoon I could hardly stand being in the shop. Since I began using energized water, my health has improved rapidly. My legs are not swollen anymore and I was able to almost stop taking pills for my circulation. My blood pressure has stabilized. I also had severe acne and for about 20 years I had to use cortisone ointments.

Now the acne is gone and I don't need to use the cortisone ointments any more.

Because of the accident my sight and hearing were also impaired and my powers of concentration also got weaker gradually. After about half a year with energized water, this impairment disappeared. Different types of therapy such as stretching the spine, electrotherapy and injections never really helped me. I think that by drinking so much energized water this has also helped wash a lot of the toxic substances out of my body and made the blood vessels in my body much more elastic. Now, after three years, I feel much better all round. My skin has become much firmer, and even old scars do not hurt as much as they used to. I don't need as many skin-care products or soaps and cleansers for the household.

"I had another experience with energized water about two years ago in Telfs in Tyrol. While we were attending an event there, three drawers from the cash register fell on my foot. The first thing I thought was that now my foot was broken! After a short break, I went back to work and around noon I finally took off my shoe. I saw that the left big toe was very swollen. My husband took me to the hospital where I was treated as an out-patient. I was supposed to stay on sick-leave until the following Monday. It was the Wednesday just before Mother's Day and we were very busy in the shop. After I was taken home, I wrapped the UVO wrist-band – a belt with tubes inside filled with high-frequency water – around my big toe and went to bed. The next morning I found I could move my toe again.

"After that, I went back to work and was able to stay the whole day. On Monday I went to the doctor's for a check-up. He looked at both big toes and I said, 'That one' and pointed to the left big toe. The doctor said, 'That's impossible!' I told him about the Grander water and the wrist-band, whereupon he replied that he didn't know anything about them."

The little town of Bad Fischau-Brunn lies about 30 kilometers south of Vienna at the edge of the so-called Mitterndorfer Senke, the biggest groundwater lake in central Europe. The water supply for some 500,000 people is drawn from it. This lake fed by groundwater has been the subject of innumerable reports in the media. This water has been plain "mucked up" by chemical companies, leaky garbage dumps and extensive agricultural activity.

The water contains heavy metal, chlorinated hydrocarbons, nitrate, atrazines, etc. in concentrations that far exceed the prescribed limits.

Since May 11, 1994, the town of Bad Fischau-Brunn, which is situated on the thermal line and has a very beautiful thermal spa, has had a mayor who has devoted a great deal of attention to the water. It was almost inevitable for Mayor Thomas Gruber to happen upon Johann Grander. "The findings of Johann Grander seem clear and plausible to me and useful as a solution to various tasks in the environmental field. Above all, the use of natural energies that permanently influence and steer our lives is what fascinates me..."

He installed Grander technology in his home and achieved results similar to those which other households had made in saving on chem-

Gabi Banitsch
and Willi Köck

Photo: Weiss

icals. Now he is working on a complete changeover to water revitalization for the whole community. He has met with political resistance, not the least of which comes from groups which call themselves "greens." Still, he is convinced: "The municipality is the ideal place for this, since it can act more flexibly and with less red tape than higher authorities can." His appeal to others in a similar situation: "Many mayors and members of town councils in Austria should muster more courage and learn something from nature. Nothing positive has ever grown from fear and doubt."

Gabi Banitsch, from Styria, Kärntner Strasse 22, 8820 Neumarkt, who operates a service station, even dared to drink water from the heating system: "Ever since I installed water revitalization from Johann Grander at my service station in August, 1994, I've noticed several interesting and astonishing changes:

1) With my brush car-wash system, I save something like up to

Photo: Weiss

Getting water to taste
from the central heating

40% on car shampoo, chemical pre-wash and up to 20% on gloss dryer.

2) Now very dirty shop windows and the insides of the car windows (nicotine) are cleaned with nothing but pure water (cold, except in winter).

3) For a year now, there has been a bottle of Grander heating-water concentrate in my heating system. To my knowledge, the water circulating in the heating system has not been changed in the last six to seven years. A few days ago, I noticed something very remarkable. When I opened a screw on one of the heating units, the purest, most odorless water was in my heating system. I even tasted it. It tastes very good and the most important thing is that I'm still alive!"

# CHAPTER 11

# The First Step towards Learning the Secret

Whenever there is a general discussion on the subject of Grander technology, there are three expressions in the air: "water as a carrier of information," "water's memory" and "erasing information." These catch phrases represent three ideas that appear to be relatively abstract. If we ask a scientist what they mean, the answer we can expect is not likely to be what we could call generally understandable, at least not to a readership with practically no previous training in this area. In the following chapter an attempt will be made, together with Dr. Horst Felsch, to work out explanations for these terms. We hope these explanations will be so simple and graphic that we will succeed in making an even deeper impression of what this totally new technology is actually capable of doing. The conversation repeated here should also provide a stimulus and an incentive for everybody to give more thought to the phenomenon of water. Everyone who thinks about water seriously will personally come a bit closer to discovering water's secret. And for him or her, water will never again be "only" water. Instead it will be seen as a puzzling, beautiful, phenomenal living creature that takes on an infinite number of forms: calm in a glass, invigorating as a drink, endlessly vast at the seashore, quiet and reassuring at a lake, exciting in a turbulent mountain torrent. And perhaps one or the other of these individuals will also succeed in communicating with water, be able to exchange ideas, to absorb its energy or simply feel joy at the sight of it. Anyone who has ever thought about water very intently is a step closer to nature and its secrets, is more attached to nature, on more intimate terms with it.

Water is the source of life. Even in the accepted opinion of science, water is nothing less than a "miracle," an element that ought to take the form of a gas, according to all that is known about the laws of physics. It is the presence of a single hydrogen bond, that is, the connection of two water molecules, that makes life on this planet possible. Dr. Felsch: "Because water as an $H_2O$ molecule should, according to everything we know about the periodic system, be gaseous; but since water is not a single molecule, but is interlinked via hydrogen bonds into a big molecule - at least 400 water molecules are interlinked with one another at room temperature - water is liquid, and that's the only reason why.

"And that's the only reason why there is life on this plant and the question of why water - of all the many liquids that exist - has so many exceptions, so many anomalies, is one that concerns creation itself."

"Water as a carrier of information," "water's memory" and "erasing water information" through Grander technology - an interview with Dr. Felsch:

Question: "Dr. Felsch, the three catch expressions I just mentioned are difficult terms in themselves. It is even more difficult to make the meaning embodied in these terms easy to understand for the readers of this book. Everything I have heard or read about them so far is so extremely complicated that one would have to be a chemist, physicist or other kind of natural scientist to understand any of it. That's a pity, since an insight into the Grander technology and the resulting 'Aha!' effect is something that is kept from us to a great extent. Is there no way to explain these difficult terms so simply and clearly that the readers of this book, most of whom are not specialists, can grasp them?"

Dr. Felsch: "That's not easy, but I can try, even though scientists are basically afraid of oversimplifying something because then it might not be completely accurate. We'll put this fear aside for the moment.

"Let's begin with the catch phrase, 'water as a carrier of information.' As in the theater, we will present this explanation in three acts, like a play. In the first act, I will explain to you what happens when

154

table salt is dissolved in water. In the second act, how the molecular construction of the water should be viewed. And in the third act, we put both subjects together and talk about the salt dissolved in the water and what the water does with the dissolved salt particles and how the information, 'this solution contains table salt,' is arrived at. Good, let's start with Act 1.

"Table salt has the chemical formula NaCl. The chemical expression for table salt is sodium chloride. A molecule of table salt thus consists of an atom of sodium and an atom of chlorine. And now the question arises how this sodium is connected to the chlorine. That is easy to imagine. The sodium has an arm and the chlorine has an arm. You, Dr. Kronberger, are the sodium atom, you extend your delicate journalist's hand to me and grasp my sinewy chlorine hand. This connection - or bond - changes the properties of the sodium and the chlorine totally. The sodium is no longer the aggressive alkali metal that forms hydrogen when it connects with water, and the chlorine is also no longer the deadly gas of the First World War, merely a completely harmless chloride.

"But this bond between the sodium and the chloride is not completely harmonious. You can already see that I am pulling you towards me with my hand. The chloride has a stronger negative electron charge than the sodium, that means it wants to pull the bonding electrons closer to itself and take them away from the sodium. In such a case, the chemist speaks of a so-called ion bond. So much for the construction of the table salt molecule.

"As you know, table salt is a solid substance, it crystallizes into lovely cubes, like those that can be seen so nicely in the salt exhibitions in Hall or in Hallstatt. What happens now when this solid salt comes in contact with water? It dissolves; the solid salt disappears and a solution is created that tastes a little salty. What happens to the salt molecule? When it falls into the water, the water molecules start to penetrate the crystal lattice and they take out the individual molecules and separate these bonds between the sodium and the chlorine.

"The chlorine, with a stronger negative charge, pulls the pair of bonding electrons over to it completely and thus becomes a chloride anion, that is, it has a negative charge because it has one electron more (which it took away from the sodium). On the other hand, the sodium is now one electron poorer, it becomes a cation, which is an ion with a positive charge. And now, one of the difficulties is already arising: since positively charged and negatively charged particles attract each other, the sodium cation and the chloride anion should approach each other again immediately. This coming together is prevented by the water molecule. In its purest form, water is a non-conductor, an insulator, and it places an insulating layer of water around the positively charged sodium ion and the negatively charged chloride. Scientists call this hydration. In the process, heat is even released. Through this hydration, a stabilization of the sodium ions and the chloride ions comes about and both can now swim around quite freely in the solution. This can be proved by inserting two electrodes attached to a source of direct current into this salt solution. On the negatively charged cathode, one actually gets the precipitation of sodium ions, which immediately react further and form soda lye (aqueous sodium hydroxide). At the positively charged anode, the chloride ions precipitate and form chlorine gas.

"That's the end of the first act. We'll proceed to the second act and observe the structural composition of the water molecule.

Question: "All we know from school is that water has the formula H2O, that is, a molecule of water consists of two atoms of hydrogen and one atom of oxygen."

Dr. Felsch: "Yes, the oxygen has two bonding arms and grabs hold of a hydrogen atom with each arm. And now something similar happens to what we described with the table salt. The oxygen atom also has a high negative charge and starts to draw the bonding electrons toward it. That is, the center of gravity of the bond between the hydrogen atom and the oxygen atom is not exactly in the middle between the two. Instead, it is closer to the oxygen atom. By having these bonding electrons closer to it, the oxygen gets a slight negative charge. But because of this, the two hydrogen atoms become poorer and so they get a slight positive charge.

"Now there are two charges present in this water molecule and for that reason water is also called a dipole (two poles, the positive pole at the hydrogen atoms and the negative pole at the oxygen atom).

From the outside, the water molecule is electrically neutral. It is only in its inner structure that it has this displacement of polarity, due to the differing negative charges of the two atoms of oxygen and the atoms of hydrogen."

Question: "What effect does that have on the molecular structure of liquid water?"

Dr. Felsch: "If a water molecule is a dipole, then the logical conclusion is that a second molecule of water can not cuddle up to the first one in just any old fashion any more: because of the polarities, the negatively charged oxygen would more likely make friends with the positively charged hydrogen in the water molecule nearest to it. And in fact these two do make a so-called hydrogen bond. It is a very delicate but still a very present bond of two water molecules. In it, a bond between the negatively charged oxygen of the one molecule and the positively charged hydrogen of the other molecule takes place.

"So. the water molecules are connected with each other through the hydrogen bonds. Research tells us that about 300 to 400 water molecules are connected together through hydrogen bonds at room temperature. And that is very decisive, decisive to life, I would even say. Because seen this way, water does not have the formula $H_2O$, it is in reality a grand-molecule, namely $H_2O$ 300 to 400 times, and thus the molecular weight of water is also not 18, namely the sum of 16 = oxygen plus 2 for hydrogen, one for each atom, but the molecular weight of liquid water at room temperature is actually 18 times 400, and that results in a molecular weight of 7,200."

Question: "Can you also explain that in practical terms?"

Dr. Felsch: "Yes, you see water in its liquid state is a super-molecule. And it has a net-like structure and the reason for that is the dipolarity of water and the resulting hydrogen bond. If water were only $H_2O$, that is, monomolecular, then it would have a gaseous state at room temperature. It would have a boiling point of minus 100 degrees Centigrade and a freezing point of minus 120 degrees. It is only because of this hydrogen bond that it is liquid, because it is a giant molecule, and for this reason alone, life has been able to develop on earth. All living structures contain water in some form, but the water has to be liquid. If it were a gas, there would be no life.

"So you see how important this special form of water structure is. In ice, this net-shaped water structure has a very regular form. It can be observed especially well in the beautifully shaped snow flakes. Scientific literature mentions that there are between seven and twelve different shapes of snowflakes. When the ice melts and the water gets warmer, some of these long-chained water molecules break up into smaller aggregates which are called clusters. These aggregates consist of 300 to 400 water molecules. And the fact that they actually do exist can be proven with x-ray and neutron diffraction and also with infrared and raman spectroscopy. Ludwig and Kokoschinegg reported on this in the 1980s.

"When water evaporates, then its structure, that is the water net, is largely destroyed. Water vapor or steam consists of two molecules of water at the most. In other words, the orderly arrangement in the structure of water decreases along with the increase in temperature. The reason for this is the so-called Brownian motion of molecules: the motion of the particles in a liquid when it is warmed. This motion causes the somewhat delicate hydrogen bonds to tear apart. The clusters get smaller, the motion increases and a constant process of reorientation takes place.

"That's the end of act two.

"And now the curtain goes up on the third act. We bring the salt dissolved in water together with the knowledge we now have about water in order to make it easier to understand how water can become a carrier of information. First a reminder: because of the table salt dissolved in the water, it contains sodium ions which have a positive charge and chloride ions which have a negative charge. As I said before: these ions are surrounded by a water envelope which acts as a kind of insulator. My concern at this point is: in view of the dipole character of the water molecule, how does it place itself around the sodium ion or the chloride ion? The sodium ion is positively charged and therefore the water molecule has to surround this ion with its negatively charged oxygen side and not the other way around. If the positively charged hydrogen in the water approaches the positively charged sodium ion they would repel each other. Therefore, there is no alternative. For the chloride ion which is negatively charged, it is the other way around. Here the water molecule as a dipole has to position itself so that the hydrogen atoms which have a slight positive charge have to attach themselves to the chloride ion while its negatively charged oxygen faces the other side. But here you must understand that the so-called water coating, the hydration envelope, around the positively charged sodium ion is built differently from the one surrounding the negative chloride ion.

"Now it depends on how big the surface of the sodium ion is before you can answer the question how many water dipole molecules can crowd around it and get close to its surface. That can be ascertained exactly. Eight molecules converge around the little sodium ion. The chloride ion is much larger than the sodium ion; nevertheless, only three water molecules surround it. Chemists call the number of water molecules that encircle an ion the hydration number.

"And now we have to think ahead logically. Eight molecules of water are docked around the positively charged sodium ion in such a way that the oxygen is adjacent to the sodium ion and the two hydrogen atoms are spread out at an angle of 105 degrees. What happens to the next water molecules that would like to attach themselves with hydrogen bonds to these eight water molecules around the sodium ion?

"And now comes the really important statement. An ion, in this case a particle of salt dissolved in water, determines through its charge and the size of its surface the way the water molecules have to arrange themselves. When the first hydration envelope is already occupied, then all the other water molecules have to keep to the same order or arrangement. This order is carried on further for many, many steps.

"Let's get back to the chloride ion which is negatively charged. There are now three water molecules docked at it, in such a way that the hydrogen atom sits on the surface of the chloride ion and the oxygen atom branches off from it at an angle. In the next hydration envelope, hydrogen atoms attach themselves to these oxygen atoms by way of hydrogen bonds.

"In the finale of the third act, the theme, therefore, is: around each ion dissolved in the water, there is a water envelope that is very specific for this ion, and it consists of dipole water molecules. Because of the hydrogen bonds, the shape these water molecules take around the ion have a lattice-like structure. The living organism, for example a human being, is trained to be able to recognize such water structures. And he knows, therefore, that when the water structure has a particular make-up, it means that a sodium ion or a chloride ion is dissolved in it. Because each of these ions have a specific hydration structure. And if we spin this thread further, then it is enough for the body alone to be able to recognize the water structure and it does not have to penetrate the center to make certain that there is really a sodium ion or a chloride ion present.

"Now it is possible to understand how water can be a carrier of information - what are we saying - can be? It is not only a carrier, it is absolutely the best carrier of information that exists, since there is no better substance for a solution than water.

"When a specific hydration envelope forms around a dissolved molecule in the water, then the information about the substance that is dissolved in the water also lies in this particular structure. And here we also have the basic idea behind homeopathy. In the original solution, something was dissolved and a specific hydration envelope built up around this dissolved molecule. And interestingly, this hydration envelope is preserved even if the solution becomes very thin. That can be explained this way: if I thin out a sodium chloride solution, for example, then I will find that sodium ions or chloride ions are much less frequent in the solution. This has the advantage that the net-like structure of the water will no longer be impeded by the one or the other ion. The net-like structure of the sodium ion will no longer be impeded by the completely different net-like structure of the chloride ion. And thus it becomes clear that the greater the degree of dilution the clearer the structural information of the original dissolved particles which is spread throughout the system becomes. (This is a quote from the professors, Resch and Gutmann, on page 207 of the book "Water," by Ivan Engler.)

"This greater uniformity of the structure of water in diluted solutions can also be proven by a number of methods, including the so-called relaxation time spectrum. This spectrum becomes more clearly delineated the more diluted a solution becomes. Here the question arises why one has to shake up the solution every time it is diluted. This dynamization is very essential. One can ascertain that the solution gets slightly warmer when this is done and, contrary to henry's law, more gases are released despite this, such as carbon dioxide in the air and oxygen in the liquid. Through this shaking, one forces the molecules already present in the solution and the newly added released gas molecules to make contact with each other. In shaking, one pushes them against each other so that they finally talk to each other. Now the released gas molecules, completely lacking in information, entice information from the molecules of the original substance (to use the formulation used by Resch/Gutmann); these gas molecules are what spread the information at hand throughout the entire vibrating system. The better this coordination works, the better the information in the original medication is spread and preserved.

"The two professors carry out the following experiment: if liquid metals are stirred or beat vigorously at the beginning stage of crystallization, then products with completely new properties form during further cooling: greater hardness, greater durability and greater resistance to distortion. We also know that sharpening a sickle by hammering it results in changes in the structure.

"If a drop of water falling through the air is confronted with harmful gases caused by environmental pollution, a part of this $SO_2$ or $NO_2$ is dissolved in the water and a water structure specific to this molecule is built up in the water. When the falling water finally collects in brooks and rivers, a large degree of dilution takes place, but also a dynamization in the homeopathic sense. The flowing of the water provides the kinetic energy used for dynamization. Because of the additional dissolved gases, this information is even stabilized. Therefore, the water contains a wealth of different information that it acquires from the time it receives the raindrop to when it runs out of the water tap in our homes.

"According to tests made by Engler and Kokoschinegg in 1988, water has a structural memory and a structural variability, and because of this it can store acquired information over a long period of time and hand it over to the body.

"One aspect of this is very astonishing indeed: at 37.5 degrees

Celsius, that is the human body's operating temperature, water has the minimum specific warmth and the maximum structural possibilities through a practically infinite number of structural combinations."

Question: "What does that mean?"

Dr. Felsch: "Specific heat refers to the quantity of heat energy that must be added to a gram of water to raise the temperature by one degree. While I was going to school, I still learned the definition of a calorie as being the amount of heat required to raise the temperature of one gram of water from 14.5 degrees to 15.5 degrees. If the water measures 37.5 degrees, considerably less heat energy has to be added to achieve a temperature increase of one degree. This would be an indication that water has a very specific structure at exactly this temperature and that this structure is in a position to acquire a large amount of information. If you heat water further, then its capability for transferring information is lessened and its memory is partially erased. Distilling water brings about an almost total erasure of this information. However, the condensation water that is formed during cooling after the distillation absorbs new information again immediately, for example, information about the material the distillation apparatus is made of.

"But let's retrace our steps and look at the water that runs out of our water taps. I have mentioned that this water contains a wealth of different information, which corresponds in essence to the water's past history. Now the question arises whether our bodies actually take over all of this proffered information and react to it. Our sense organs and probably our body's entire information system is concentrated on maintaining the health of the body and protecting it from harm. Our eye makes us aware that there is a step we could stumble over. Our nose warns us not to eat something that smells rotten. The tongue functions in a similar way: it warns us when something does not fit into our patterns of taste. We work with our information system focused selectively on the health of our bodies. Thus it can be assumed that faced with such a great variety of information offered by water, the body also accepts selectively only the information that is useful to it and possibly does not even recognize the rest. This would be wishful thinking. Actually, the fact is that some of that information does reach the body even though it is harmful. The body accepts this information because it is camouflaged or is indistinguishable from the other."

Question: "What does that mean, applied to the human body?"

Dr. Felsch: "Let's consider a virus infection. The virus itself is not a living thing, but consists of genetic information, that is of DNA or RNA. The virus itself has no metabolism and is also not able to produce anything. If the virus attacks a human cell, its RNA or DNA is injected into the cell via a mechanical process. And now something highly interesting happens. At first the cell is completely confused about what it should do. Should it continue to reproduce its own proteins, in accordance with the information in the cell, or do what the newly injected viral DNA or RNA commands? The latter apparently has a greater influence on the cell since the cell forgets its own construction work and suddenly produces viral DNA or RNA. And that is the way an increase in the virus takes place.

"We see, therefore, that a virus illness has a great deal to do with erased information. A cell goes astray in its production and suddenly listens to the whispers of the virus's genetic substance. The cell produces and reproduces these viral substances and, in the end, dies because of them. But the viral information is already in the blood stream and by the time the body's own defensive mechanism takes notice of this malfunctioning, massive contamination has already taken place. Thus, illness or health in the body also depend on information that is transferred to it.

"More than 150 years ago, a man by the name of Samuel Hahnemann made homeopathy what it is today, namely a recognized method of healing. He called illness an alteration of information that occurs at the highest level, there where the soul comes into contact with the body. For him there is no illness that does not also have an influence on the soul, or mind. A virus, to come back to our example, that cannot be incorporated by the body with its information system must therefore lead to a corresponding malfunction in the organism. If the body does not succeed in counteracting this misinformation with the help of its own defense mechanisms and erasing it, the person remains ill. If the body were to accept all the information that water or the sense organs offer it, then the volume of the information would become infinitely vast and that would necessarily lead to a breakdown of the organism. It is the selectivity that enables it to stay healthy. Medicines can erase the illness-information in the homeopathic sense. And it is the homeopathic high potentials that have such sharply delineated individual bits of information that they are able to uncover foreign information and then to make it harmless.

"According to Hahnemann, the medicine must be chosen so that its information content is as similar as possible to that of the agent that makes one ill." Everything depends on the similarity of the information content and only the similar can be healed with the similar - hence the so-called 'law of similars'.

"Now the extremely important question arises whether the information contained in Grander water is also able to uncover information that is likely to be harmful to the body. The many, partially amazing cases of successful healing with Grander water, which you, Dr. Kronberger, have put together in this book, would suggest the conclusion that this does actually happen. We do not have scientific proof for this, but I can offer something else. In a special chapter, you have described my experiment in which I was able to kill off microorganisms in a circulating heating system within six weeks by using the Grander technology. What happened? These microorganisms had to live under the most unfavorable conditions imaginable: temperatures up to 52 degrees, an alkaline pH value of 10 and for food there were only highly molecular chemical compounds that were really intended to prevent corrosion.

"As it happens, microorganisms have an unbelievable ability to react quickly to bad conditions, because of their short generation period. Whereas for man, a generation is reckoned as being from 30 to 40 years under optimal conditions, it is 20 minutes for microorganisms. Under poorer conditions, this generation period is lengthened to several hours. Nevertheless, microorganisms are able to collect information and to pass it on to the following generations. Bacteria, especially, have a kind of information back-pack. This backpack is made up of something called called plasmids, a term coined by Lederberg in 1952. This plasmid information backpack holds the

164

information that tells bacteria how they can develop a resistance to heavy metals such as cadmium and mercury, how to cope with ultra-violet light and also how to metabolize carbon from unusual sources, that is how to make them usable for their metabolism.

"The microorganisms present in the pipes I was concerned with therefore had a thick plasmid backpack which contained all the information about how to survive at high temperatures, how to hold their own against alkaline pH values and how to use almost indigestible foods. In my opinion, these bacteria died off under the influence of the Grander technology because most of this resistance information was erased. Suddenly 52 degrees was much too hot and the pH value of 10 much too alkaline and they did not know what to do anymore with the source of carbon that was available to them. So they had to die. I cannot think of any other explanation for the bacteria dying off, since we did not add anything to the water. It flows through these energizers without direct contact and it gets indirect information which is apparently able to erase existing bacteria information."

Question: "If that is possible with bacteria, shouldn't it also be possible to erase information when we're dealing with drinking water?"

Dr. Felsch: "If the Grander system is also capable of erasing information that is harmful to human beings in drinking water and other systems, then we have here, for the first time, a technology that can reduce the endless flood of information that inundates the human body and through this, help it to stay healthy.

"I must admit that I am still moving in the sphere of speculation with this theory. But on the other hand, it is not all that speculative. There is no doubt that a relationship between information and health exists. Of course, with ideas like these, we are entering a new realm of thought in science. The Nobel prize winner Werner Heisenberg addressed this subject very aptly in his book published by Piper Verlag in 1969 under the title "Der Teil und das Ganze" (transl: "The Part and the Whole") in the following statement:

'...Truly new ground in a science can only be broken if one is prepared at a decisive point to leave the ground upon which previous science has stood and to jump into empty space, so to speak.'

"In chemistry there are also many examples of scientists not being accepted at first when they entered new territory. Two examples: in 1874 Jacobus van't Hoff claimed that the construction of the molecule had to be pictured spatially and not in the usual two-dimensional structure of a page in a book. That was rejected with the argument that in principle, this three-dimensional character could not be detected (because at that time, it was impossible to see into molecules). Even in 1917, it went against the common patterns of thought when Gilbert Lewis advanced the idea that chemical bonds could be formed with the help of a pair of electrons.

One example from medicine: the Austrian university professor and renowned physician, Karl Spitzy, attributed the healing effect of homeopathy for a long time to the "charisma of the doctor." Later he changed over to accepting it as a placebo effect. And it is in fact amazing that up to 30% of the healing rate has been proved to be attributable to a placebo effect. The prerequisite, however, is that the medication be prescribed or administered by a doctor (the so-called 'white coat' effect) or by someone with a high scientific reputation. So we see that even here, healing is accomplished via information systems.

"In 1993 the university professor, Dr. Herbert Pietschmann, from the Institute for Theoretical Physics at the University of Vienna gave a very interesting interview with the Austrian apothecary's newspaper.[7] I quote: 'Natural science set out in the 17th century to describe matter in time and space and achieved marvelous successes in the attempt. However, these successes had their price, and the price was this very aspect of limiting matter in time and space. Everything that cannot be explained as matter in time and space cannot be explained scientifically. It is possible to state that simply and clearly. But that means that we in medicine can scientifically explain and describe all the aspects of the process of healing, of the illness or even of health itself - which have all been thoroughly studied already - if we reduce people to their bodies alone, that is, to their matter in time and space. Everything that goes beyond that, which involves spiritual-mental aspects as well - I quite intentionally do not speak of either-or, but

---

[7] ÖAZ, 47th year, Number 20, October 2, 1993, p. 745

where these aspects are inseparable - can fundamentally not be completely explained in scientific terms.'"

Question: "Can I draw the conclusion from this that even physics is still a long way from arriving at a point that can be called 'conclusive'?"

Dr. Felsch: "You can see that despite all the simplification, the subject is still very complicated. But Heisenberg spurs us on to be courageous and open-minded in science, and to dare the jump."

Question: "In closing, even at the risk of being repetitious, I would like to ask you once again for a brief, everyday summary - or should I call it your minimal definition - of Granderwater, seen from a strictly scientific point of view."

Dr. Felsch: "If I climb down from this high ladder of theory and come back to reality, then I can pinpoint three things.

"First: Granderwater is not a medicine. You have stated that several times in this book. Granderwater has a thirst-quenching effect - that is the only official health-related effect.

"Second: at present there is one expertise on the absolute safety of Grander water revitalization devices built into drinking water systems. There is also confirmation of absolute safety in terms of hygienic (under the terms of the food law) and technical aspects. For every new technology, proof that it cannot cause harm must be established. This proof has been furnished.

"Third: for me the most interesting aspect is the practical use of the Grander technology. It is an absolutely 'clean technology,' the kind we desire in environmental protection."

At this point, the authors of this book would like to reveal what were for them the most fascinating results of their search on the track of water's secret. They were simply the little experiments made with a potted plant on the desk, the application on a bee sting or use in the dog's bowl of drinking water, filled alternately with enlivened water and plain water. The results are a private matter, and only this much is revealed: experimenting is fun. If you should have experiences of your own with enlivened water, we are grateful for every pointer. One day there is sure to be a continuation of the search for clues...

# Acknowledgements

This book was "energized" by the following persons (in alphabetical order). Without their help, their knowledge and experience it would not have been possible to create this book in this way. We extend our sincerest gratitude to them:

Wolfgang Allertshammer, Heinz Breuer, Horst Felsch, Franz Gegenbauer, Johann Grander, Georg Huber, Marlies König, Peter Ortner, Fritz Rauscher, Jörg Schauberger, Klaus Schoch and Ladislav Toth.

# Bibliography

**Alexandersson, Olof;** *Lebendes Wasser.*
Ennsthaler Verlag, 2nd edn, Steyr, 1994.

**Engler, Ivan** (ed.); *Wasser.* Sommer-Verlag, Termingen, 1991.

**Gagelmann, Hartmut;** *Mozart hat nie gelebt.*
Eine kritische Bilanz. Herder, Freiburg, 1990.

**Kronberger, Hans;** *Das Rätsel des Wassers.*
Serial parts 1 - 7, SONNENZEITUNG, 1994-95.

**Lorek, Kurt** (ed.); *Implosion.*
(Nos. 7, 11, 12, 49, 67, 88, 104), series of biotechnical writings,
Windschlägerstrasse 58, D-77652 Offenburg.

**Ludwig, Wolfgang:** in *Umweltmedizin.* Edited by
Treven/Talkenhammer. Möwe-Verlag, Idstein, 1991.

**Pietschmann, Herbert;** *Ende des wissenschaftlichen Zeitalters.*
Weitbrecht-Verlag, Stuttgart, 1994.

*Wasser und Information,* Aspekte homöopathischer Forschung.
Edited by the Institut für Strukturelle Medizinische Forschung e.V. and by
the Physiologisches Institut der Universität Graz. Karl F. Haug Verlag,
Graz-Heidelberg, 1993.

**Will, Reinhold D.;** *Geheimnis Wasser.* Knaur-Verlag, Munich, 1993.

# Addresses
# of UVO Centers

The network of companies and persons providing further information and product is steadily growing.

To get the actual list of companies, persons and distributors in your region pls. contact the address relevant for your region.

**For USA and Canada:**
Dan Stewart p. eng
    1850 Victoria Ave East
    Regina, Sask. CANADA
    S4N 7K3
    phone toll free: 1-888-333-6616; fax: 306-789-3977

**For South East Asia (including Australia and New Zealand):**
Full Comfort
    8, Hillwood Road
    Fiat A-B, 8th/FL, Glory Centre
    Kowloon Hong Kong
    phone: ++852-2314-2608; fax: ++852-2317-5687

**For Europe:**
UVO-Vertriebs KG
    Pfarrhuegel 293
    A-6100 Seefeld i. T.
    phone: ++43-5212-4192-0; fax: ++43-5212-419228